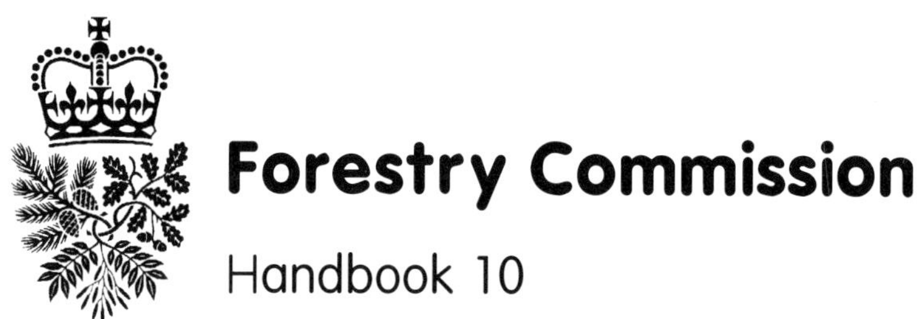

Wildlife Rangers Handbook

Editors:

G D Springthorpe BEM
Former Head Ranger and Wildlife Adviser

N G Myhill
Former Senior Ranger

It is the duty of us all to speak up and protect wildlife and their habitats, to treat the land as though we will live for ever, so that future generations may enjoy the beauty we have had the pleasure of knowing.

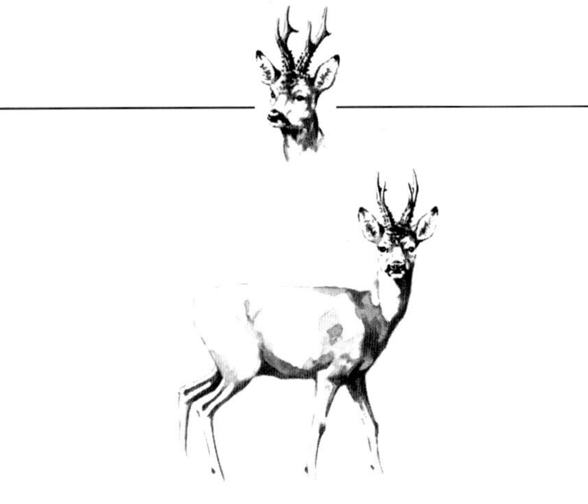

Paintings and drawings
by Neil McReddie
61 Scotby Road, Scotby, Carlisle, Cumbria

Design: Margaret E Morgan BA
Front & back cover: Geoff Morgan/Photography
Print: Crewe Colour Printers Ltd
Typesetting: Formecon Services Ltd
Colour origination: Four Color Litho Sets Ltd

First published by the Forestry Commission 1985
Reprinted with minor amendments 1994

ISBN 0 11 710326 8

Acknowledgements

The editors wish to acknowledge the following rangers for their contributions: D Clement, C Critchley, L Cropper, J J Cubby, G M McReddie, M Noble, M Pearson, P Pursglove, G Rostron. Also H Insley *(District forest manager),* J Kingsmill *(Forester),* M J Potton and H M Davies *(Graphics and design),* Mrs Knowles and her typing staff at Chester Office, Miss J J Rowe and Mr P R Ratcliffe Wildlife Branch, Research Division, Mr D Pointon (photographs) and the staff at Alice Holt Research Station. The production of the book was made possible through the direction of Mr A A Rowan, Conservator NW(E), and Mr N Dannatt, Assistant Conservator NW(E).

Prefaces

Gerald Springthorpe worked on deer control for the Forestry Commission before his army service and became as worried as I and many responsible members of the public were about the treatment of wildlife on forest land. When he was demobbed he was invited to join the Commission as a warrener, which he hoped would give him the chance – and responsibility – of improving the lot of the wildlife he loved. Senior management in the Commission co-operated and so he was trained by Herbert Fooks, a distinguished authority on wildlife management. Wildlife rangers from all over the country came to Cannock Chase for training, and Gerald acquired an international reputation, giving advice here and on the continent, especially on fallow deer management.

He discovered a strain of long haired fallow deer at Mortimer Forest. Thought to be unique, these deer are now widely known as *Dama dama springthorpeii.* They might have been exterminated but for the timely help of Patrick Cormack, FSA, MP, who intervened to prevent the sale of land in the middle of the forest, which is vital for their survival.

Like attracts like and Gerald was a magnet for the best type of wildlife ranger, including Nick Myhill, who studied languages at Oxford until the instinct for getting his feet on the land triumphed over previous ambitions. So he left Oxford and did two years farming before joining Gerald as one of his rangers, specialising on habitat management. His academic background fitted him for co-operating as co-editor with Gerald to produce this Wildlife Rangers' Handbook.

It is based on creative conservation at Cannock by the group of enthusiastic men Gerald gathered around him, with active help and approval at top management and Conservator level within the Forestry Commission. As a manual *by* working wildlife rangers *for* working wildlife rangers, it will benefit shy and endangered wildlife and the public who can now enjoy them. More scientific treatises may appear in future but I predict that nothing will surpass this as a practical manual.

Phil Drabble, OBE

Editor's preface

In the past 8 years or so, since this Handbook was first published, the perception of nature conservation has evolved considerably, so that it is questions of tone and emphasis as well as facts which have changed. After consideration and consultation, it was decided to let the book stand with its original style, with only simple errors, omissions and developments altered in the new edition.

Other changes have occurred in the outside world. Attention is drawn to the following:

- The application of laws on 'Health and Safety' affecting the ranger has developed, not least with regard to the handling of deer carcasses. The booklet *The Culling and Processing of Wild Deer* by John Adams and Norman Dannatt (Forestry Commission and Arun District Council 1989) is recommended.

- Section 7 'The ranger and the law' has been left in its original form, with brief notes on pages 118 and 124 on some changes in firearms and wildlife law between 1984 and 1993.

- Some environmental agencies referred to have been reorganised, merged and retitled. Notably the former 'Nature Conservancy Council' is now known under separate titles in various parts of mainland Britain: Scottish Natural Heritage, the Countryside Council for Wales, and English Nature (the national countryside agencies). Most of the functions of the former regional Water Authorities referred to in this book (such as regulation of works to lakes, watercourses and fisheries) have been assumed by the regional divisions of the National Rivers Authority.

G D Springthorpe, BEM and N G Myhill, July 1993

Contents

Foreword

The very survival of most of our native species depends upon the care and sensitivity of the farmer and the forester, and on their willingness to think and plan in decades, if not centuries.

Since the end of the Second World War the Forestry Commission, the nation's largest landowner, has given an increasingly good example of proper conservation practice. That this is so is due not merely to enlightened management in Edinburgh but, even more, to the skill and dedication of local foresters and rangers who care deeply about the creatures, and the plants, without which no forest can truly live. Of all the men and women who have worked for the Forestry Commission no one has a more distinguished record than Gerald Springthorpe and his pioneering work on Cannock Chase has been recognised throughout Europe.

I was a very new Member of Parliament when I first met Gerald in 1970. He came to one of my advice sessions with a local naturalist who was already something of a household name, Phil Drabble. They quickly became greatly valued friends and I am delighted that Phil has written the Preface for this splendid handbook in which Gerald and so many of his colleagues so clearly and generously share their experience and skills.

Looking through its pages I am taken back to those days in the early 1970s when I spent many happy hours on The Chase with Gerald, observing deer from his skillfully constructed hides and learning how important culling is to conservation; watching the woodland birds and seeing how he encouraged them to nest; admiring, with some trepidation, the care he took to ensure that The Chase's population of adders were protected, without the many thousands of visitors to the Chase being put to undue hazard. For Gerald forestry was not a career but a life, and he and Phil, who abandoned a lucrative career in industry to create his own wildlife reserve in Staffordshire (and who recently won, in conjunction with the Forestry Commission, a Centre of Excellence Award for good conservation practice) taught me so much.

During my time as Chairman both of my Party's and of the All Party Parliamentary Forestry Committees I have become ever more conscious of the need to ensure that whatever policies Governments put forward everything must be done to ensure that the owners of our woodlands are encouraged to practise far-sighted conservation management so that our woodlands and their priceless wildlife flourish. For all those committed to such conservation this handbook will continue to be an invaluable guide.

Patrick Cormack, FSA, MP

Section 1
The ranger and forestry

A. Introduction to forestry

B. Basic skills

C. The ranger's calendar

A. Introduction to forestry for the wildlife ranger

The purpose of this chapter is to give a brief outline of the principal objectives of forestry in the United Kingdom and to describe the framework within which the wildlife ranger will work. Whilst there may be different degrees of emphasis between the objectives in private and state sectors of forestry, these will have little practical effect on the wildlife ranger's duties.

Over the past centuries various Royal Decrees and Acts of Parliament have led to the definition and creation of forests and woods for a variety of purposes, from the provision of animals (mostly deer) for hunting, to the supply of timber for ship-building, to establishing a strategic reserve for use in the time of war, to the present day where the principal objective is to provide a raw material for industrial use. The major requirements (over 90%) of the United Kingdom timber industry is for softwood (that is to say timber from conifers) for paper and packaging products, and for materials used in the construction and mining industries and others. Over 90% of the timber we use is imported at a cost (in 1984) of over £3,000 million. The great majority of the conifer woodlands have been established on poor soils in the uplands with some on the infertile lowland heaths. Broadleaved woodland is concentrated in the lowlands of England where the soils are richer and the climate less harsh. The largest proportion (72%) of broadleaved woodland is owned by private individuals and not included in either the Forestry Commission Forestry Grant Scheme or the Dedication and Approved Woodland Management Schemes. The table opposite shows the land ownership by woodland type, and clearly illustrates the major challenge to the wildlife ranger to enhance the wildlife value of coniferous forests in partnership with the forester, whose primary objective is to provide the raw material for this country's industry, and thereby improve the general standard of living. Protecting and enhancing the conservation value of broadleaved woodlands is no less important, indeed the intrinsic value of broadleaved woodlands, because they grow in a kinder climate and on better soils, is often higher than that of conifers, but the task is usually conducted on a smaller scale.

The primary practical task of the forester is to manipulate the local environment to produce the maximum output of timber at the least cost, and this establishes the framework of constraints and opportunities within which the wildlife ranger works. However, this is subject to 4 secondary objectives, any one of which may, in special circumstances, supersede the primary objective. These are; to protect and enhance the environment, to provide recreation facilities, to stimulate and support the local economy in areas of depopulation and to foster a harmonious relationship between forestry and agriculture. It is quite clear that a considerable part of the justification of forestry activities lies in the unique opportunities for wildlife management and leisure pursuits on a large scale. The essential point about any industry like forestry with several objectives, is that the various aims must interact, and not be carried out in isolation from one another. A good example of this is the way in which forests are designed. Originally, it seemed simplest to plant trees in straight-edged compartments drawn from a map, but this has proved to be, firstly, visually unacceptable, secondly, often providing a weak point from which windthrow develops, thirdly not providing suitable access routes for fire fighting or harvesting operations, fourthly, not allowing for efficient deer control, and so on. Today compartments are designed to fit into the landscape of the area, the boundaries being natural features such as streams with their associated broadleaved trees or roads, and it is no longer practice to plant right-up to the forest fence. Similarly rides are laid out to blend with the landform and are sometimes associated with areas of broadleaved trees which have been established to enhance the wildlife potential of the area. The result is an improved type forestry with benefits to timber production, to wildlife, and to the lover of the countryside in general. One of the greatest challenges of forestry is that progress can only be made by co-operation between the various interests, and this may be the hardest lesson that the ranger has to learn.

The forest district manager and his staff have overall responsibility for all activities within the forest, and it is their duty to plan operations so that they enhance the wildlife

Area of woodland by forest type ownership

Forest type	Forestry Commision area	Forestry Commision % of total	Dedicated and approved area	Dedicated and approved % of total	Other area	Other % of total	Total area	Total % of total
Mainly coniferous high forest	819303	91	377649	74	119856	17	1316808	62
Mainly broadleaved high forest	54132	6	101320	20	408966*	58	564418	27
Total high forest	873435	97	478969	94	528822	75	1881226	89
Coppice with standards	32	<1	4544	1	6992	<1	11568	<1
Coppice	1000	<1	4504	1	22060	<3	27564	1
Scrub	5751	<1	12082	2	129682	19	148235	7
Cleared	11498	1	11968	2	16339	2	39805	2
Total	891716	100	512787	100	703895	100	2108398	100

NOTES: * *This figure for mainly broadleaved high forest contains 14.9 per cent of coppice origin.*

value of the forest or have the minimum adverse impact, and in this way they will look for the assistance and specialist advice of the wildlife ranger. There is a team working within the forest district structure each of whom have specialist responsibilities for the various activities within the forest, and the wildlife ranger must understand the demands of these other activities so as to take his place within the team. Mutual respect for each other's objectives will ensure a good working relationship which in turn will have the best consequences for wildlife.

As part of his introduction to forestry at the beginning of his career a wildlife ranger must gain a good appreciation of all aspects of forest work. The best way of achieving this is by actually doing the job and passing as many of the appropriate skills tests as is practicable. It is particularly important that he should gain proficiency in the use of all the machines and tools that are used in the establishment phase of a crop of trees, because he cannot carry out his duties, for example, without being able to repair a fence. Thus in the first year a trainee wildlife ranger will spend much of his time on other forest duties. Whilst this aspect of his work will diminish as he concentrates on his wildlife duties, he should ensure that he keeps up-to-date with improvements in techniques and methods for all relevant forest operations. If the ranger is qualified to use the chainsaw, clearing saw and tractor, these skills will be of immense use to him and to his forester in, for example, preparing deer lawns or undertaking conservation tasks. On the other hand it should be possible by co-operation with foresters to arrange for essential tasks (such as ride-swiping to aid crop protection) to be carried out as part of the forest work programme.

Forestry is unique as a profession because the overall objective is to grow a crop over many decades. Whereas farmers think and plan for a 12-month cropping cycle or, in the case of animal husbandry, for a few years at most, foresters need to think in terms of a 60 or 100 year crop cycle. The production of a renewable resource over such a long time span brings its problems for the forest manager, for example, when considering the implications of capital invested for such long periods of time, and any mistakes made in forest plans may take decades to rectify. But this long-term perspective also brings considerable opportunities in the planning of forest operations for the benifit of wildlife over a period of years, examples being the protection of rutting and nursery areas of deer, badger setts, nesting or lekking sites for the more uncommon birds, eg goshawk, blackcock and specialist plant and insect communities, all of which are dealt with in detail in this book.

During the seasonal cycle of the year, to neglect the proper timing of some operations could be disastrous for either the tree crop or wildlife in general. Several examples spring to mind; the timing of control measures against the grey squirrel is crucial to the success of the protection programme; the timing of the swiping of certain rides, where it is best done every other year to allow insects to complete their life-cycle, or carrying out pool maintenance in autumn to minimise disturbance to wildlife; and even more importantly, knowing that it is a mistake to inspect batboxes during the winter, as this may cause their death. The job of the ranger is a craft carried out in sympathy with nature, and this training manual is intended to start the ranger in the right direction as well as provide him with up-to-date information.

Not only is a wildlife ranger responsible for advice and carrying out his duties within the forest boundaries, he has a key role to play in fostering good relations with neighbours. There are many facets to this aspect of the work, and the emphasis is different in different parts of the United Kingdom. A good example being the attitude of neighbours to the fox, which does no harm to forest crops, but which is vigorously pursued by the hill farmer because of alleged damage to his lamb crop, but which is protected for hunting in the lowlands. The rabbit is a universal pest both to farmer and forester alike, although in the later stages of the life of a stand of trees this animal does no damage, but must be controlled in the interest of good neighbourliness. Deer do not recognise property boundaries, and the best possible management can only be carried out in most situations when the ranger makes his practical knowledge and expertise available to neighbours. Indeed, the most responsible way to manage a deer herd which ranges over the property of several owners is by mutual co-operation and sharing experience and knowledge.

As the wildlife ranger becomes more expert in his job he will need to acquire the skill of communication. There is an increasing awareness of the conservation value of woodland, and it is essential that the practitioner is able to inform the general public through the medium of lectures and guided walks, and also to demonstrate the many facets of his work in the forest. This requirement brings wildlife and recreation rangers together, it being most likely that the latter have a considerable interest in wildlife and it is thus essential that they also understand the opportunities and constraints of the job as a whole. The wildlife ranger has the responsibility of developing trails within the forest in association with recreation staff, to demonstrate aspects of wildlife management to the general public, and particularly to school-children.

Over the years wildlife rangers will develop a wide knowledge of many aspects of natural history, but as it is unlikely that they will become really expert in all but a few, they will therefore, along with their forest district colleagues, need to establish and foster relations with the many public and voluntary conservation bodies. The public bodies with responsibility for nature conservation are the three national countryside agencies and official liaison is maintained at all levels of the Commission organisation, but the links with voluntary bodies are less formalised. The County Nature Conservation Trust with their United Kingdom co-ordinating body, the Royal Society for Nature Conservation (RSNC) is very important, as are the Royal Society for Protection of Birds (RSPB), the British Trust for Ornithology (BTO), the British Association for Shooting and Conservation (BASC), the British Deer Society (BDS), the British Herpetological Society, the Mammal Society, the Archaeological, Geological and other Societies. Many of the members of these organisations are knowledgeable and can be most helpful to forest managers and wildlife rangers by increasing their knowledge and understanding of the specific subject, and hence lead to better management practices. For example, it should be made clear to such bodies that if they are aware of sensitive conservation sites on Forestry Commission land, the time to inform the Commission of these is before planting, when allowances can be made in the forest plan, and not afterwards, when it is only a question of recriminations. In other cases the ranger may feel that activities such as bird ringing or insect collecting are not compatible with the conservation objectives of a particular area. This is the sort of advice which he can take to his forester, who will also expect similar feedback from the ranger on sporting tenants. It is also true that a very few members belong to societies and organisations for their own selfish reasons, for example to gain knowledge where rare butterflies or birds of prey may be found, or where they may gain preferential treatment for deer stalking. The wildlife ranger should make every effort to foster relations with these organisations, but must be aware of the odd few members whose motives are not compatible with his duties.

It will be clear by now that the work of a wildlife ranger, like that of a forester, is partly a way of life with standards of loyalty, honesty and dedication required that are higher than in many better-paid occupations. Because of his position, the ranger must always be seen to set a standard in wildlife management which the general public, landowners and other bodies may look to. The demands of this vocation are considerable, especially in the spread of hours during the day. The ranger also has his fair share of responsibilities, such as the safe use of the rifle. Only those of the highest calibre and dedication can expect to carry out the duties of a wildlife ranger properly. At the same time it should be clear that the challenges and satisfaction of forest wildlife management are equally high and rewarding.

The wildlife ranger's job can be summed up as being a member of a team whose special responsibilities are to act as the eyes and ears of the Forestry Commission, to protect crops in and around the forest, to see to the welfare of wildlife and to identify wildlife sites so that their value may be perpetuated and, if possible, enhanced through the habitat manipulation which is the essential role of the forest manager. To do this he must be able to communicate with management and the general public, and foster good relations and respect with neighbours and all interested parties.

B. Basic skills

The wildlife ranger has one of the most widely skilled jobs in the forest. Most of these skills are covered under the main subject headings of this handbook (eg 'Crop protection', 'Deer management', 'Conservation') but first there are a few basic skills which the ranger must acquire or understand at an early stage of his career.

(i) Care of animals

The ranger's dog is both close friend and indispensable assistant. The choice of breed (terrier? German pointer? labrador? dachshund?) is partly determined by the type of work undertaken by the individual ranger. For all the training and breeding in the world most rangers will look back on one dog in a lifetime which stood head and shoulders above the rest in natural ability. What can be said is that the ranger must set a standard in the care and treatment of his dog, and all other animals, which reflects his professional standing and privilege to work with animals.

At an early stage in his job, the ranger should spend a few days if necessary in building a spacious pen and kennel for his dog which can be kept to a high standard of cleanliness and has a hard outdoor run which can be swilled out regularly. The bed in the kennel should be raised at least a foot off the ground (this keeps the dog out of a draught) and there needs to be a board to lie on in the outdoor run as well. Bedding should be clean wheat straw or bracken, and needs to be changed regularly to avoid flea infestation. (Fleas are also the host parasite for the tapeworm).

At a week to a fortnight old is the best time for the vet to remove dew-claws (a necessary operation for most working dogs) and to dock the tail (if appropriate) to a reasonable length. At 4-5 weeks puppies must be dosed for roundworms, and at 6 months for tapeworms, thereafter twice yearly for tapeworms only, more frequently if working rabbits regularly. At 8-10 weeks you should take your dog to the vet for the first course of his multi-vaccination.

In your van there should be a dog-guard to prevent the dog jumping into the front. (When you leave your dog in a vehicle during hot weather, it is essential to allow adequate ventilation and a bowl of water, especially if the dog has been working. Also leave the vehicle in the shade).

It is a good policy to leave dogs at home when visiting a keeper at the time of nesting, also when working in the immediate vicinity of his pheasant pens. Do not take your dog with you when any kind of gassing is in progress, or if you suspect the presence of any poison on the land. Always check with local keepers when and where fox-wires are being set. If your bitch is in season, leave her at home if you will be in the company of other working dogs.

Ferrets, like dogs are valuable assistants to the ranger, it is essential that they are handled regularly to maintain familiarity with their owner and they must be housed in good conditions. Ferrets should be kept in a spacious hutch with 2 separate compartments, one for sleeping and one (wire-fronted) for eating. It is best to keep the hutch in the open, in a sunny site sheltered from wind, so the hutch needs to have a sloping, felted roof. The roof must of course open on hinges. The inside of the hutch should be smooth (ie exterior framework) and painted for ease of cleaning. The end of the feeding compartment furthest from the sleeping compartment should have a strong wire grill or perforated aluminium base, and the ferrets will use this as a latrine. The whole pen should be strewn with sawdust, with a handful of soft litter (not a great pile of straw) in the sleeping quarters. All of this should be scraped out every other day, and all food scraps meticulously removed (for which purpose both compartments should have opening fronts). Ferrets are not dirty animals, it is their owners who sometimes keep them in squalid conditions. In particular ferrets should not have to live on wet floors with stale carrion lying around. For this reason water (or bread and milk) should be provided in heavy untippable bowls, alternatively water can be provided in the type of drinker available from pet shops for rabbits. Meat is best hung up securely to prevent the ferrets dragging it into the sleeping quarters, and should never be left for more than one day. Carcasses must be paunched. Ferrets need fresh food at least once daily. If ferrets were provided with reasonable living conditions, the common diseases (distemper and foot-rot) would be unknown.

Ferrets (except liners) like company so keep at least two (a line ferret is a large hob (male) which is usually kept separately). Remember that females (jills) should be mated on their second heat, or else they will be short-lived. For breeding you will, of course, need at least two hutches. For further details of ferret management, see publications such as *Rabbiting and Ferreting*, the British Field Sports Society booklet.

But it is not just in the care of working animals that the ranger may be judged. His attitude towards all creatures, including those which it is his duty to cull or despatch, must be unwaveringly humane. Any act of cruelty or deliberate disregard for animals must automatically disqualify a person from holding a ranger's post. The ranger must also avoid any obvious mistakes of animal handling, such as hand-rearing a male deer as a pet which become highly dangerous when fully grown.

(ii) Use of firearms

Along with the care of animals, the use of firearms is a subject in which it is always necessary for the ranger to exhibit the highest standards. Firstly the ranger must know the law on firearms (see Section 7 B). Secondly, he must observe all legal and commonsense points of security. The Forestry Commission ranger's firearms must be kept in a locking steel safe which is bolted to the wall or floor in his house. Rifle bolts and ammunition should be kept in locking safes separate from the main body of the rifle. The ranger is well advised to carry the keys to his firearms safe on a chain in his pocket, with a spare set deposited, for example, at the forest office. The ranger's van should have a locking safe if rifles are being carried. In any case a firearm left inside a vehicle must be out of sight, bolt removed and the vehicle locked. The ranger's firearms certificate or Crown Exemption Certificate should also be kept in a safe place. The security of firearms and the procedures for acquiring and storing ammunition should be laid down in the health and safety plan for the forest. Thirdly, the ranger must observe all points of safety.

Never point any gun in an unsafe direction, whether loaded or not. Always carry a shotgun with the barrels down towards the ground, always carry a rifle barrel skywards and sling forward. The two main times when you check that a firearm is unloaded are when you pick it up or receive it (in the morning, or from someone else) and when you put it down or part with it (in the evening, in your van, when handing it to someone).

A firearm should be completely unloaded in any building, when being transported in a vehicle, when left unattended. It is acceptable to have ammunition in the magazine only of a rifle, provided you have checked positively that there is nothing in the breach, when climbing a high seat, when crawling through or climbing over obstructions, and when travelling on a forest road only with the rifle beside you. It may be loaded, on safety, only when you are sitting, walking or stalking. With a shotgun, you break the barrels at least when negotiating any obstacle. You may stand or walk, when expecting to shoot, with the safety-catch on. In any other situation, the shotgun must be completely unloaded.

- You should only release the safety-catch immediately before firing. Do not fire unless you know the background to be safe. After firing, the usual drill is to reload and engage the safety-catch.
- Do not leave a firearm propped up (against a wall or a tree). Do not put it down in the forest and leave it, eg to pursue something.
- Keep ammunition dry and clean while it is stored and carried, preferably carry rifle ammunition in a bullet pouch, and shotgun cartridges in a belt. Do not ever risk mixing up different calibres of ammunition. It is inadvisable to own two rifles of different but similar calibre. This avoids any possibility of ammunition becoming mixed up with potentially disastrous results.
- Always have your firearm checked by a registered gunsmith at least once a year, preferably during your slackest period, but

immediately if you have any doubt about its function and after any occasion when the weapon has been accidentally knocked.

● Dry and clean your firearm before putting it away. Do not over-oil the trigger and safety mechanism. Store firearms barrel downwards after any oiling. When you first acquire a new firearm, apply linseed oil to the wood, and thereafter avoid getting excess gun-oil onto the woodwork and in the bedding gap.

● Zero your rifle regularly.

● Finally, do not ever fool around with any firearm under any circumstances. Do not even give your gun to someone to look at unless this is necessary.

For further information, see Section 4 J.

(iii) Getting to know the forest

One of the first steps for the ranger is getting to know his forest. During the ranger's trainee year, the forester, head or senior ranger should provide the trainee with a map of his area, and allow time for him to walk the area thoroughly.

During this part of his training, the trainee ranger should get to know neighbours and landowners, keepers, farmers, forest workers, rangers from neighbouring organisations and any others with a direct interest in his area.

The trainee should learn his boundaries and get to know all details of the tenure for the area he is responsible for, especially the detail of any restrictions on wildlife control and any sporting rights and he should take careful note of areas in which it would be dangerous to shoot, eg because of a hidden road.

He should begin to mark on his map any pieces of information which will be of use to him, and thereby take first steps to drawing up a wildlife map, as this is one of the best ways of getting to know the area.

He should look for areas of crop damage and begin to learn to recognise the difference in appearance between healthy and unhealthy trees. He should learn to identify all common trees, shrubs, wild flowers, insects, birds and other animals in his area, with the aid of identification guides (see 'Recommended reading' at end of handbook) and of fellow rangers and naturalists.

Getting to know your forest is a task which is never completely achieved, but the foundations to this knowledge should have been laid during the trainee year, and before the ranger begins to concentrate on crop protection duties.

(iv) Use of poisons

The use of poisons by the ranger is as much a responsibility as is the use of firearms. Because of the ranger's responsibilities to wildlife and to users of the forest, he is also expected to be alert to the possibility of misuse of poisons by others.

Be sure the poison is legal for the use to which it is being put (see Section 7 C ii) in contrast to the use by some misguided keepers of insecticides such as Phosdrin for the purpose of killing vermin which is clearly illegal. Be sure poisons used by the Forestry Commission are kept in a locked, steel-doored cabinet at the forest chemical store. Be sure equipment for applying poison (eg spray equipment) is rinsed at the appropriate place in the forest depot, and not in the forest at pools, streams, etc. Be sure surplus poison is disposed of safely. Be sure poison is not being applied where its use is illegal or has been banned by voluntary agreement, eg watersheds to water supplies, in primary woodland and SSSIs.

Consult the Forest District Safety Statement on the use of any poison you have dealings with. When using any poison, you must have been instructed in the use of that poison by the head ranger, forester-in-charge, research forester or other qualified person. Be sure you understand the instructions correctly, and that you have every item of safety equipment with you, eg masks, gloves, protective clothing. Always carry any necessary antidote. Always work in pairs if required to do so (eg when gassing rabbits). Always carry washing equipment. Always transport the poison in the agreed manner. Never keep more than the amount of chemical needed for one or two days work, and never accumulate half-used containers of chemical in your store.

If you find any wildlife specimens which appear to have died from poison, lift them into a plastic bag without touching them, and take them to your Veterinary Investigation

Centre of the Ministry of Agriculture, Fisheries and Food (MAFF). If you find poisoned bait illegally placed on FC land you should alert the police and keep watch over it, in an attempt to catch the user.

(v) Ranger equipment

The ranger's equipment should always reflect credit on its user or owner, both by being the right equipment for the job, and by being kept in good order.

The essential equipment for any wildlife ranger, other than his firearms, consists of a vehicle with first-aid kit, binoculars (preferably 7 x 50 which have adequate magnification and good light gathering characteristics for work in poor light conditions), identity card, knife, notebook, pencil, radio and whistle. The ranger should have appropriate clothing, ie waterproof coat and trousers, non-slip wellingtons, uniform, camouflage jacket, overalls, boots. A rucksack is essential for carrying the first-aid kit, identity card, whistle, knife binoculars and 'drag bag'. The latter being essential for carcass extraction of the larger species of deer. When travelling into remote parts of the forest, the ranger should have the appropriate survival equipment (see next paragraph).

When involved in deer work, the ranger should also have a van, firearm safe, blood-tray (preferably plastic and designed for that vehicle), a vehicle searchlight, a hand torch, a rifle cover, scope covers, ammunition pouch and face mask or scarf. A vehicle winch or even special cross-country vehicle may be essential for carcass extraction in some circumstances. The deer larder should be purpose-built, easy to clean, and equipped with butchering knives, wooden chopping board, scales, dustbins, twin sink, hosepipe, disinfectant and broom.

When involved in rabbit work, the ranger should have snares, good purse nets, a ferret bleeper or a good line and collar, rabbiting spade and possibly long-nets.

The van should be kept clean by washing and (if necessary) disinfecting at intervals, as it is a major presentation of you and your employer's image. Remember essential van maintenance = WOFT (Water, Oil, Fuel, Tyres).

(vi) Health and safety

Every forest must, by law, have a Health and Safety statement, and the ranger should read this, and request for its amendment if necessary. Some points affecting rangers in particular are:

- Safety helmets should be worn when inspecting bat boxes and bird boxes, especially by anyone standing at the bottom of the ladder to steady it. Helmets should also be worn when working beneath high seats while they are being erected or pulled down.
- Permanent high seats should be built to strong specifications with suitable timber (eg larch, not untreated pine). Ladders to high seats must by law be wired down the side-struts and across the rungs. Large high seats should be bolted together not nailed. Seats built higher than 3 m from the ground must have an annual engineering inspection. Old high seats should be pulled down before they become unsafe.
- Forest pools should not be built with steep slippery sides from which dogs and even children may be unable to climb.
- Rangers going into remote parts of the forest, especially in upland areas, should carry a small survival kit, eg chocolate, survival bag, whistle. Rangers should devise a system so that someone is aware if they do not return home. They must have a radio in their vehicle.
- When using firearms, rangers should use ear protectors. These should be worn at all times, and not just on range work. Be particularly careful to protect your ears while you are supervising someone else with a gun.
- Rangers should be aware of the risks of catching the tick-borne lyme disease, of how to take preventive measures against tick-bite, and of symptoms associated with the disease, eg a rash spreading from a tick-bite, flu-like symptoms.

This is obviously not a comprehensive list of safety precautions.

C. Ranger's calendar

January

Inspect plantation for: vole damage; stripping by deer; blackgame and caper damage.

Concentrate on doe/hind cull especially where damage is occuring.

Continue rabbit control, including snaring and ferreting.

In snow: track down rabbits, hares and deer in fenced plantations. In unfenced areas, dog rabbits into holes then gas.

Check agricultural crops adjacent to the forest, particularly root crops.

February

Beginning of February liaise with landowners to complete doe and hind cull where pheasant shooting has held it up. Concentrate deer cull on areas where damage is occuring.

With pheasant shooting over and cover down, concentrate on rabbits in keepered areas during February, March, April. Last of ferreting before young rabbits born (according to season); snaring; dog then gas.

Check all rabbit and deer fences, free badger-gates. Check agricultural root crops (eg swedes) for deer damage.

Inspect plantations for stripping and browsing by deer, voles, rabbits, hares, blackgame, etc. Note annual drift of deer, record on wildlife map.

March

Deer on fields and open plantations, this month and next. Ideal time to round off buck/stag cull. Apply to take extension to doe season, if necessary.

Consider heather moorland management, burn (or swipe) as necessary.

This is time for deer census and counts, with more sightings of fallow, red and sika than any other month. Liaise with landowners concerning deer census.

Also involve landowners in bird and bat box schemes. First bat box inspection. Inspect and clean out bird boxes. Other conservation work (eg coppicing) finished before nesting season begins.

Deer preparation room and cooler-room should be cleaned and scrubbed down. Leave cooler-room door open when not in use.

April

Roe buck season opens – work hard on early cull.

Concentrate on areas vulnerable to deer damage: young plantations and vulnerable agricultural crops.

Rabbits: finish off control before green flush begins. Concentrate on areas near farmers' fields.

Squirrel control should be under way in areas which experience serious damage.

Best time for re-seeding deer glades. Check all salt and mineral licks.

Deer census finished off, cull figures agreed, arrange annual deer meetings.

Assist neighbours with fox control, where necessary.

May

Squirrels: peak of control season. Every trap and hopper must be out where severe grey squirrel damage occurs. Make damage assessments at the end of the month (check crowns of trees with binoculars). Also inspect for beetle damage, especially pine weevil.

Maintenance: creosote hutches and kennels.

Look out for illegal poisoned eggs and baits on keepered areas of forest!

End of month damage assessment for deer.

June

Grey squirrels still top priority.

Keep deer nursery areas (especially fallow) free from disturbance, eg by orienteering.

Assess wildflowers in woodlands; check arrival of migratory birds; work on wildlife maps.

Oversee any bird-ringing done on Forestry Commission ground.

Put in guns for annual check.

Do high-seat building/maintenance.

Remind forester: best time of year to carry out upland drain maintenance without harm to spawning fish.

July

Check gas levels in fridges and coolers.

Prepare for shows and exhibitions.

Stags in season in Scotland (red, sika, hybrid).

Roe rut begins.

August

Get male deer cull under way early in season (red, fallow, sika). But keep carcasses free from flies!

Roe rut ends.

Finish all squirrel work early in the month. The use of Warfarin must stop by 15 August. Lift and store traps/hoppers. Ensure poison bait and poison is locked away.

Record on wildlife map all sensitive areas eg wildflowers, reptiles and amphibians, butterflies.

Rabbit-shooting in fields during harvest. Visit forest compartments vulnerable to damage. Check for spread of rabbits and hares, decide on management for forthcoming winter.

September

Work hard on male deer, cull surplus fat bucks and stags before rut. Deer to be found on stubble fields and under hardwoods gorging on chestnuts and acorns.

Fallow and red returning to traditional areas from summering grounds.

Mow grass rides for rabbits and deer control – this is particularly important on muntjac areas for their effective management. (Alternate sides of ride mown annually for conservation).

Make arrangements for arrival of permit stalkers.

October

Complete roe buck cull, now they are showing again. Red and fallow rut. Visit rutting areas for census assessment. Try to avoid culling on main rutting stands.

Forest pool maintenance. Other winter conservation work can start (eg coppicing).

Last bat box visit of the year. Do not disturb boxes again until April!

Concentrate on rabbit control.

November

Concentrate on female deer cull until end of February, taking out late and weak fawns and calves first. Cull on damage and re-stocked areas first. Most deer ruts coming to close by mid-November, but sika last of all.

Rabbits: with the long nights begins the peak of the snaring season, from now till March. Good time of year to long-net.

Do you have any budget requests? Now is the time to ask.

December

Important for all deer culls except roe bucks. Sika stags herding again.

Rabbits: ferrets should be working, with no young rabbits about.

Keep a keen eye for Christmas tree thieves. Have night patrols for deer poaching if necessary.

Section 2
Wildlife and conservation

A. Forestry, wildlife and the ranger

B. Introducing wildlife habitats

C. Recognising primary woodland and its species

D. Managing primary woodland for conservation:
   i. Coppice-with-standards
   ii. Wood pasture
   iii. Caledonian pine

E. Birdboxes and batboxes

F. Reptile conservation areas

G. Pools, wetlands, amphibians and dragonflies

H. Heath and moorland

I. Traditional species (badgers, eagles, etc)

J. Grass rides and verges

K. Insects

L. Species adapted to conifer woods

M. The wildlife map and conservation plans

N. Conservation planning —
   NW(E) technical instruction

A. Forestry, wildlife and the ranger

Something which rangers are quick to appreciate from their work is the need for forests to be designed properly, that is to say with more than their obvious timber-growing considerations in mind. This may mean the management of forest rides, or not planting up an area of wetland, or leaving strips of natural vegetation either side of forest streams, or even just a few dead trees for woodpeckers. These forest areas will diversify the habitat for wildlife (a major objective of conservation), and mostly have some of the following advantages: Assist crop protection from fire, wind and animal damage; provide improved recreation facilities, whether of a specialised (eg fishing, wildlife photography) or general nature; improve the appearance of the forest from a landscape point of view.

On the other hand, it should be understood that there are some areas or features on the forest whose conservation value is considered irreplaceable, eg areas of primary woodland, breeding sites of threatened species such as sand lizards or a rare butterfly, blackcock leks, bager setts. In these cases they will be protected and managed for conservation irrespective of any other advantages. Two points arise from this situation:

(i) Conservation must take priority on these areas in any clash with other activities. In particular, it is often a great mistake to imagine that conservation and recreation can always be lumped together. Instead the whole forest should be considered from an overall perspective, with separate zones for general recreation, specialised activities such as fishing or wildlife photography, and for conservation. It needs to be better understood by forest managers that the public will see more wildlife in the long-run if wildlife is given the unspoilt habitats it needs to survive, and sanctuaries to breed undisturbed, and then come out onto the wider forest and be seen.

(ii) A management plan should be drawn up for conservation areas to provide continuity when forest staff change. (Several, but not all, conservation areas will already have been designated by the national countryside agency as Sites of Special Scientific Interest — SSSIs. In other cases Forest Nature Reserve agreements have been made with the agency and special management constraints may apply).

It should be remembered that on most forests all the forest design areas and conservation areas put together will only make up a tiny fraction of the total forest area. Furthermore, there are often corners of the forest on which trees cannot be grown profitably in any case, eg wetlands, stream gulleys, quarry holes, inaccessible areas of woodland. Any cost to the Forestry Commission is, therefore, reduced, whereas the wildlife values of the whole forest can be improved enormously, provided that the key wildlife areas are selected in the first place. This is why a survey and assessment of the whole forest needs to be undertaken, with information also gathered from any outside bodies or individuals. As this is the basis for wildlife conservation, and the ranger is ideally placed to make a major contribution, the chapters of this section concentrate on habitat assessment as well as management for conservation.

To summarise: A primary duty of the wildlife ranger is to have a good knowledge of the plant and animal life in his area. Foresters will expect the ranger to assist with, and initiate, the conservation work carried out by the Commission, in which the usual steps are:

- A survey of the habitat and species of the whole forest, usually accompanied by drawing up a wildlife map for the area.
- Careful selection of conservation areas which have such an outstanding value to wildlife that they should be managed primarily for this purpose, with a management plan for each of these areas.
- Development of forest design areas to break up the forest for wildlife and other purposes. (These are also considered in detail in Sections 4 F and 6 B of the handbook, as they are equally relevant to crop protection and sporting management.)
- Ensuring that normal forestry practices show consideration to wildlife, eg avoiding the misuse of chemicals dangerous to the environment, planting native trees on amenity areas, not building forest roads into sensitive wildlife areas, not using sensitive wildlife areas for other activities which will clash with conservation aims, especially recreation and sporting. Draw up a zoning plan of land uses for these purposes.

B. Introducing wildlife habitats

The ranger's preliminary task is to be able to understand the conservation value of the different habitats such as oak woodland, pinewoods or heathland. These need to be seen as webs of species depending on one another which have been produced by a particular combination of geology and climate.

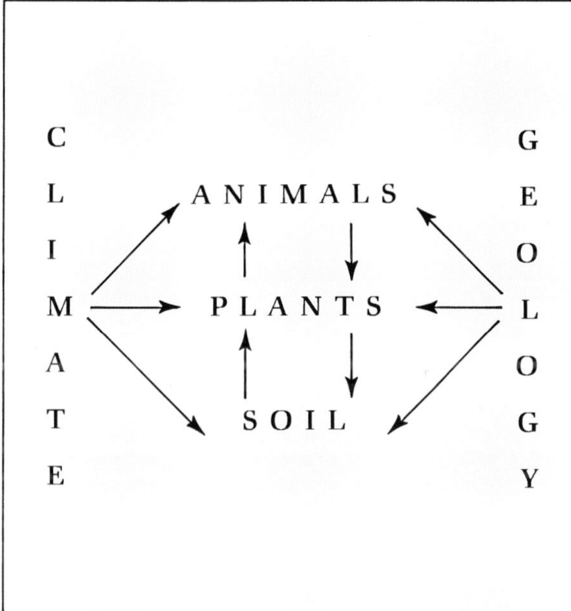

The habitats we see around us today are partly formed by a third major influence — Man.

In order to understand how the natural habitats have been altered and preserved by Man, we should take a brief look at their recent history:

10,000–5,500 BC — As the last Ice Age receded and the climate gradually improved, Britain was recolonised by waves of species, eg the first trees were birch, followed by pine, hazel, elm, oak, alder and lime, in that order. The process continued until the cutting of the land-bridges (from the Continent to Britain, and from Britain to Ireland, which hindered further colonisation, eg lime, weasel, woodpeckers and adder failed to reach Ireland; beech marten and black woodpecker failed to reach Britain.

5,500–3,100 BC — The native habitats remained relatively stable. The dominant habitat was woodland, simply because where they can grow, trees dominate other vegetation types by sheer size and long life. As well as woodland much of the lowland area of Britain was wetland.

3,100–400 BC — Stone Age Man avoided the wet, heavy lowland soils and his effects were mostly limited to the well-drained light soils and upland areas. Heathland and moorland became much more widespread as a result of clearance in these places, perhaps aided by a cooling of the climate.

400 BC–1200 AD — The arrival of iron tools, notably the axe and plough, led to the remarkably rapid clearance for agriculture of most of Britain. By 1086, when the Domesday Book was written, only about 15% of England remained wooded.

1200–1700 AD — This remaining woodland was entirely under human management in England by the 13th century; in Wales soon afterwards, though in Scotland some woods have remained unfelled and ungrazed until the 17th century. The major woodland management systems of coppice with standards, coppice and pasture woodland were established. As a result of drainage, wetlands began to disappear rapidly.

1700 AD–Present day — As Man's demands on the landscape intensified because of industrialisation, these systems began to be replaced throughout Britain by plantation forestry of the kind practised by the Forestry Commission, giving rise to the habitat known as secondary woodland.

We can now look at these different types of habitat in greater detail, and begin to consider which sites to choose as conservation areas, based on habitat assessment, and also how to manage them.

Wild service leaf – true size of large leaf from young tree

Numbers of insects and lichens associated with trees and shrubs

See *Woodlands* (British Trust for Conservation Volunteers, 1980, page 168). * = Introduced species. Order of priority for lichens is indicated in parentheses. Note that *numbers* of associated species are not a simple indicator of conservation value, as plants such as aspen and holly support a small but specialist fauna.

Tree or shrub	Associated insect species	Associated lichen species	
Oak (pedunculate and sessile)	284	324	(1)
Willow species	266	160	(7)
Birch (silver and hairy)	229	126	(9)
Hawthorn	149	no data	
Blackthorn	109	no data	
Poplar species (incl aspen)	97	no data	
Crab apple	93	no data	
Scots pine	91	132	(8)
Alder	90	105	(11)
Elm	82	187	(4)
Hazel	73	160	(6)
Beech	64	206	(3)
Ash	41	255	(2)
Spruce*	37	no data	
Lime	31	83	(14)
Hornbeam	28	44	(15)
Rowan	28	125	(10)
Field maple	26	93	(13)
Juniper	20	no data	
Larch*	17	no data	
Fir*	16	no data	
Sycamore*	15	183	(5)
Holly	7	96	(12)
Chestnut (sweet)*	5	no data	
Horse chestnut*	4	no data	
Yew	4	no data	
Walnut*	4	no data	
Holm oak*	2	no data	
Plane*	1	no data	

C. Recognising primary woodland and its species

We have seen that in Britain there is no truly natural woodland left untouched by Man, nor has there been for a long time. What we do have, however, are woods which have stood where they are since the time of the wildwood, managed by Man but never uprooted. The distinction between these ancient or primary woodlands and planted or secondary woods is vital from the conservation point of view. Only primary woods retain large fragments of the original habitat web. In particular this includes those species which are poor colonisers, and therefore tend to be rare in the changing environment created by Man, whereas they would have been major links in the stable world of the wildwood.

By the same token, these poor colonisers for example the wild service tree as illustrated on page 19, and other species highly adapted to primary woodland conditions provide us with indicators of primary woodland if they are present. (Indeed it is a very useful point of practical ecology that any species is an indicator of its habitat. A well-known example is that we expect a wet environment where alders and sedge grow, because we know they are indicators of wet habitats).

If several primary woodland indicator species occur commonly in a wood, we know this wood has a high conservation value. A list of known primary woodland plants is shown opposite for use by the ranger in recognising and assessing woodland by this method, though the list is unlikely to be comprehensive for all areas of Britain. After this there are two pages of colour illustrations showing some of the most easily recognised and well-known of these plants.

In any habitat one thing leads to another, and it is not just the plants of primary woodlands which are distinctive. For example, there is a list of primary woodland slugs and snails in the interesting Nature Conservancy Council publication *The Conservation of Snails, Slugs and Freshwater Molluscs.*

Primary woodland indicator plants

(As suggested by G F Peterken for Lincolnshire in 'Biological Conservation' Vol. 6 1976 with a few changes)

Plant	Notes
Quercus petraea (Sessile oak)	Hillsides and light soils especially in north and west
Tilia cordata (Small-leaved lime)	Mostly in Midlands on poorly drained soils
Sorbus torminalis (Wild service)	Not north of Lake District
Euonymus europaeus (Spindle)	Calcareous soils, north to Clyde and Forth
Equisetum sylvaticum (Wood horsetail)	Acid soils, commoner in north, wood pasture
Ophioglossum vulgatum (Adder's tongue)	Also in old grassland and fen
Polystichum aculeatum (Hard shield fern)	Not just ancient woodland, but shade, ditches
Helleborus viridus (Green hellebore)	Moist calcareous woods up to Yorkshire
Anemone nemorosa (Wood anemone)	Common spring flower (typical of woods) throughout Britain
Ranunculus auricomus (Wood goldilocks)	Also old grassland
Aquilegia vulgaris (Columbine)	Wet calcareous, also fens. Beware garden escapes
Corydalis claviculata (White climbing fumitory)	Acid soils
Cardamine flexuosa (Wavy bitter cress)	Wet shaded places in general
Viola reichenbachiana (Pale wood violet)	Calcareous woods
Hypericum hirsutum (Hairy St Johns wort)	Basic soils
Moehringia trinervia (3-nerved sandwort)	
Oxalis acetosella (Wood sorrel)	Light acidic soils, occasionally outside woods
Vicia sylvatica (Wood vetch)	Forms large clambering bush with pale lilac flowers
Lathyrus montanus (Bitter vetch)	Less restricted to woods in north west
Geum rivale (Water avens)	Any undisturbed, shady site. Hybridises with wood avens
Sedum telephium (Orpine)	
Chrysosplenium oppositifolium (Opposite-leaved golden saxifrage) *Chrysosplenium alternifolium* (Alternative-leaved golden saxifrage)	Rocky streamsides, especially in woodland and shade
Sanicula europaea (Sanicle)	Deep shade
Mercurialis perennis (Dog's mercury)	No obvious flower, forms what looks like carpet of spinach!
Euphorbia amygdaloides (Wood spurge)	Damp woods, not Scotland
Primula vulgaris (Primrose)	Sometimes outside woods
Primula elator (Oxlip)	On chalky boulder clay woods, east England
Lysimachia nemorum (Yellow pimpernel)	Grows on thread-like stalks
Myosotis sylvatica (Wood forgetmenot)	Damp woods
Veronica montana (Wood speedwell)	Damp woods
Melampyrum pratense (Common cowwheat)	Semi-parasitic. Acid woods, heaths
Lathraea squamaria (Toothwort)	Root parasite, especially elm and hazel
Galeobdolon luteum (Yellow archangel)	Heavier soils outside Scotland
Scutellaria galericulata (Common skullcap)	Streamsides as much as woods
Campanula latifolia (Large bellflower)	Northern
Campanula trachelium (Nettle-leaved bellflower)	Unmistakeable tall plant with blue flowers
Galium odoratum (Woodruff)	Well-drained base-rich woods, often common
Adoxa moschatellina (Moschatel)	Also mountain rocks
Dipsacus pilosus (Small teasel)	Also river banks
Maienthemum bifolium (May lily)	Very rare
Convallaria majalis (Lily of the valley)	Dry woods, mostly on limestone
Ruscus aculeatus (Butcher's broom)	Dry woods, southern, also among rocks
Endymion non-scriptus (Bluebell)	Light soils, particularly, very old secondary woods also
Allium ursinum (Ramsons)	Damp woods and shady places, especially basic soils
Paris quadrifolia (Herb paris)	Damp calcareous woods, sometimes in secondary woods
Luzula pilosa (Hairy woodrush)	Throughout Britain
Luzula sylvatica (Greater woodrush)	Also on moorland in north west
Narcissus pseudonarcissus (Wild daffodil)	Camp woods, also grassland
Epipactis purpurata (Violet helleborine)	Especially beechwoods
Epipactis helleborine (Broad helleborine)	Throughout Britain
Neottia nidus-avis (Bird's-nest orchid)	Throughout Britain
Platanthera chlorantha (Greater butterfly orchid)	Especially base-rich soils
Orchis mascula (Early purple orchid)	Especially base-rich soils
Carex laevigata, pendula, pallescens, remota, strigosa (Sedges), *Milium effusum, Calamagrostis canescens, Agropyron caninum, Melica uniflora, Conopodium majus, Hordelymus europaeus*	(Grasses)

See also species listed in connection with Scots pine on page 25

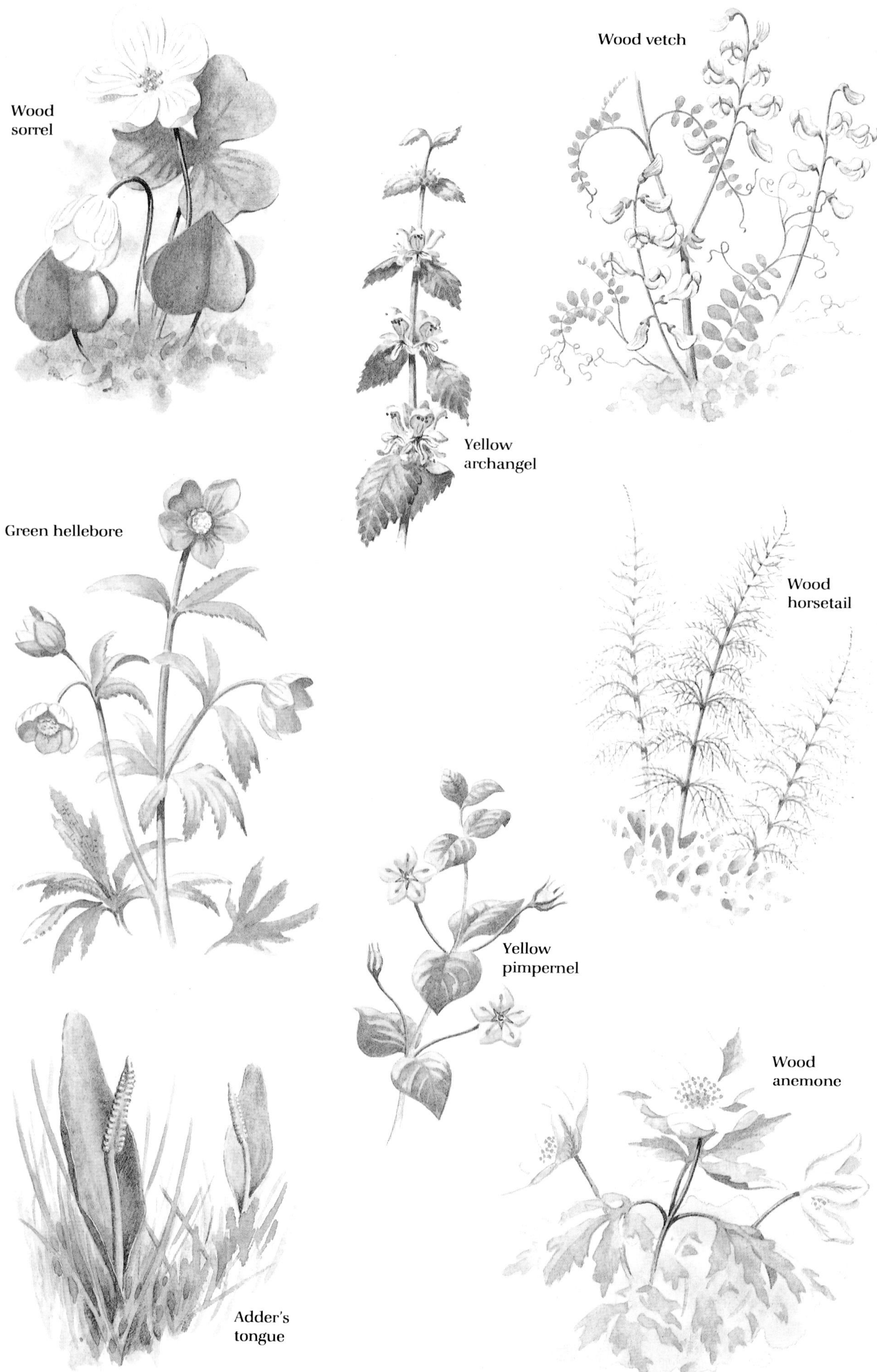
Wood sorrel
Wood vetch
Yellow archangel
Green hellebore
Wood horsetail
Yellow pimpernel
Wood anemone
Adder's tongue

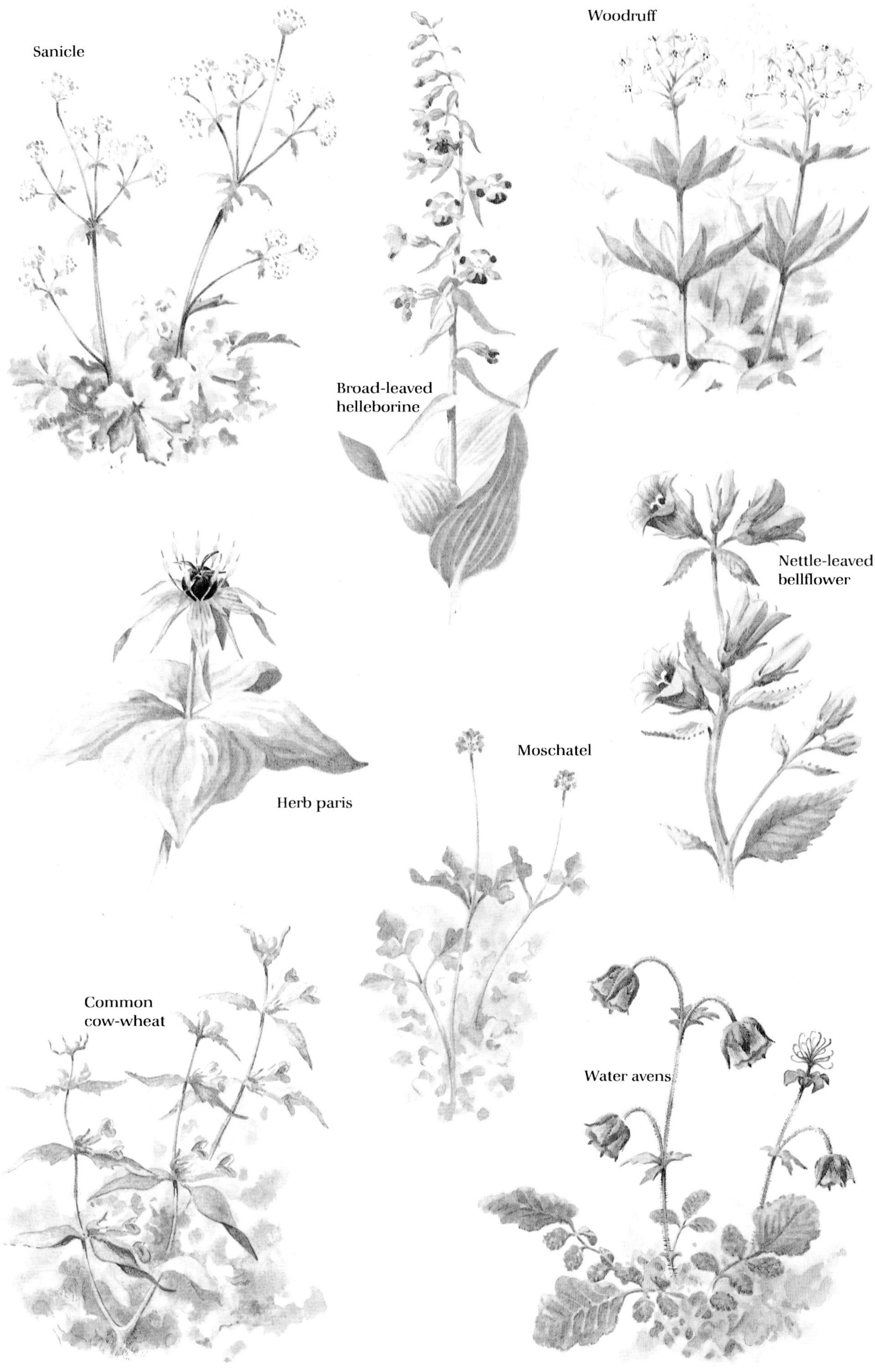
Sanicle
Woodruff
Broad-leaved
helleborine
Nettle-leaved
bellflower
Moschatel
Herb paris
Common
cow-wheat
Water avens

D. Managing primary woodland for conservation

i. Coppice-with-standards

The sort of primary wood in which the plants discussed and pictured above are most likely to occur is a coppice wood. Coppicing was the commonest form of woodland management, and relied upon the rotational cutting of regrowth to produce both underwood (the coppice) and large timber (the standards). This not only provided medieval man with a continuous supply of wood in suitably different sizes, it also provided woodland species with continuous woodland conditions in suitably different stages, and particularly a balance between light and shade. This is why we can expect to find several of the conservative ground plant species and their associated insects in a former coppice wood. It is important to recognise that this system with its attendant rich flora and fauna is entirely artificial being created by Man for his material benefit.

Much of the unique conservation value of old coppice woodland is lost if it is merely left to its own devices. Management entails:

a) Division of the area into rotation plots, each of ½-1¼ hectares, and with 7-20 plots according to the required rotation. A larger site than this may need to be considered as 2 coppices, or have larger plots divided by windbreaks.

b) Divisions should be drawn where possible on former rides to preserve old grassland flora. Where a coppice plot lies on the edge of a wood, the woodbank, another important habitat, is best cut or pleached in a different year.

c) Each plot should then be cut over to fit into a coppice rotation one year at a time. Coppice stools should be about 3-5 metres apart.

d) The number of standards on each plot has to be balanced carefully against the risk of over-shading, and depending on age and size will vary between 12 and 50 to the hectare. The latter figure would certainly include several young stems of less than 30 years. It is preferable to have standards of various ages, up to about 100 years, on each plot. The first set of standards retrieved from a neglected coppice may not be outstanding, but selection should aim at reasonably clean stems (6 m) with good broad tops. Avoid ever clearing any plot of standards altogether by retaining a few large ones while young trees are allowed to develop. Otherwise bramble will tend to choke the more vulnerable ground flora. Strike a continual balance between too much light and over-shading.

e) Further work may be necessary in early years to restore a coppice wood which has been run down. This will include: the creation of stools by cutting existing stems of suitable tree species (hazel, oak, wych-elm, lime, maple, ash, alder, hornbeam, etc. The choice of species should be determined by the type of woodland which is natural to the site, eg oak/hazel, ash/elm/lime). Also by layering, transplanting of suckers, and planting of suitable species both as coppice and standards, preferably from local seed. Where it is necessary to supplement the existing vegetation in this way, it is a good idea to undertake the work in the year following the first coupe. This is because it is more apparent where the gaps are when one year's regrowth has taken place. For further details see FC Leaflet 83.

ii. Wood pasture

This was the alternative medieval management system for timber, whereby large trees were grown on areas also grazed by stock. To produce wood these large trees were pollarded, which is the equivalent of coppicing carried out higher up the trunk, in order to be out of reach of grazing animals. Wood pasture is typically found in deer parks, commons, former royal forests and chases. Relatively few ground plants survive intensive grazing, though violets, the food plants of the true fritillary butterflies, are one of the interesting exceptions. The real value of old wood pasture is above ground level. The survival of ancient trees through pollarding transmits to us unique fragments of our native ecology in the form of epiphytic* plants, lichens, bark-living insects such as pseudoscorpions and tree spiders, as well as the hole nesting birds and bats.

Perpetuating an area of ancient trees must therefore be considered one of the most valuable conservation schemes possible, as these species associated with ancient trees have become particularly rare in the modern environment. The aim of wood pasture management is to provide continuity for these rare species, in other words to make sure there are young trees growing up alongside the old to replace them when they eventually die and decay altogether. This they should be allowed to do naturally, and never be felled if genuinely ancient.

On Forestry Commission land the normal practice would be to plant up adjacent sites with a succession of suitable hardwoods (according to the species present). If it is not possible to use adjacent land, small clearings can be made in existing wood for planting or regeneration, avoiding the felling of the best existing specimens of old trees.

It may immediately be possible to prolong the life of any younger existing trees by

pollarding. Eventually the young replacement trees may also be pollarded, preferably when the main stem reaches about 150 mm in diameter. This is an especially valuable technique when deer are an inherent part of the habitat.
(* epiphytic = growing on another plant)

iii. Caledonian pine

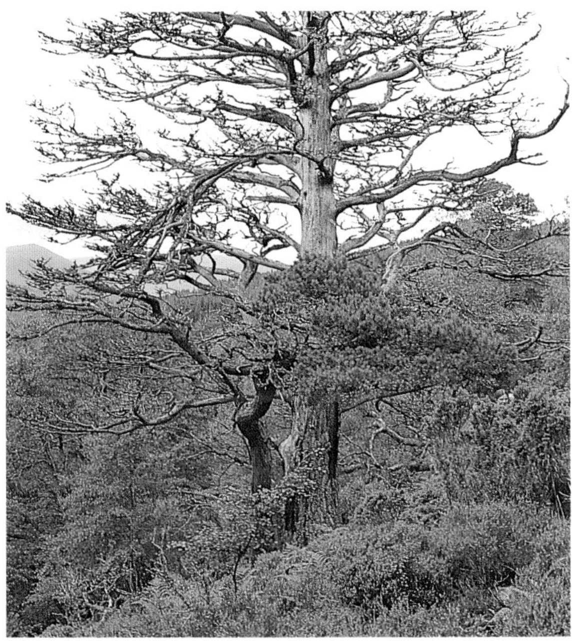

The remnants of natural pinewood in Scotland have been affected by Man in several ways (burning, over-grazing, timber extraction, pollution), nonetheless it is considered that in many respects these forests are closer to their mature natural condition (or climax in ecological terms) than any other forest type in Britain. Because human management has not been an integral part of their survival (unlike coppice woods and deciduous tree pasture), the ideal, from the conservation point of view, would be to allow all the remaining natural pinewoods to develop with no management at all, other than to protect them from any further unnatural interference.

This ideal of minimal management cannot be imposed on all surviving Caledonian forest, under present laws, simply because landowners may wish to harvest timber from their piece of Caledonian pine, or to allow more red deer to overwinter in them than will permit natural regeneration. The former Nature Conservancy Council therefore proposed that at least a proportion of each Caledonian pine forest be preserved in a strict natural zone (no management other than protection from overgrazing by deer, sheep or cattle and other influences), while other areas could be maintained as management natural zones (no ploughing, drainage fertilising or planting which would completely destroy the natural ecology, but some timber management in the form of thinning and natural regeneration) and planting zones (normal timber practices, but only pine from local origin planted, and no management which might affect adjacent natural zones).

The Forestry Commisssion, which is in a better position than the private landowner to give priority to a resource of national conservation importance over a relatively minor timber resource, is obviously playing a major part in this unique conservation plan. Agreements have already been drawn up which the ranger can consult locally for a more detailed appreciation of the subject. See also *Native Pinewoods of Scotland,* 1977, Editors Bunce and Jeffers.

In addition to some of the primary woodland indicators already listed (eg wood sorrel, sweet woodruff, hairy woodrush, dogs mercury), primary Scots pine woodlands has some associated species of its own, including: lesser twayblade *(Listera cordata),* twinflower *(Linnaea borealis),* common, intermediate and one-flowered wintergreen *(Pyrola minor* and *media, Monesus uniflora),* chickweed wintergreen *(Trientalis europa)* which is found in northerly birch woods, coral-root orchid *(Corallorhiza trifida),* creeping lady's tresses *(Goodyera repens).*

iv. Some principles of conservation management

Managing primary woodland cannot be carried out from a textbook. Books, plus discussion with experienced land-managers, provide useful background knowledge of techniques such as coppicing. But above all this must be combined with *sensitivity to what is present on a particular site.*

For example, it is wrong to imagine that every primary woodland should immediately be brought into coppice management. If a wood has never been coppiced, or was last coppiced 50 years or more ago, then it may well be that species which respond to the rotation of light and shade conditions are not present. What is more, it may be that other species *are* present which would die out if subjected to coppice management. To coppice a wood drastically for the first time, then stop coppicing through lack of resources or practicality, could cause an overall loss of species.

Rather than rush into whole-scale changes, it would be better to maintain conditions which have existed during the recent history of a primary wood, or introduce change gradually. This is particularly true for the conservation of insects and invertebrates, which adapt to micro-habitats influenced by woodland management.

E. Birdboxes and batboxes

Obviously, 90% of the woods and areas the ranger works in are neither ancient woods, nor old heathlands, old grassland nor wetlands. They are (to give them their proper habitat description!) secondary woods, that is to say woods without a continuous history of native species. In other words they are typical forest plantations, many of them (especially in the north) conifers, but some of them hardwoods, mostly in the lowlands.

The Commission ranger is not principally concerned with the argument about the rights of typical Forestry Commission woods, which is fortunate because what is far more constructive than arguing is what the ranger can actually do for wildlife in these woods. This is the reason it was essential to look at our native woodland habitats first. It is not just a question of recognising real ancient woodland if there happens to be some remaining on our area, important though that is. It is also the only way to understand the sort of habitat that British animals and plants are adapted to and require, so that we can provide it for them if possible.

A good example of this is providing boxes for hole-nesting species. Having considered the nature of the wildwood, it will come as no surprise to find that several of our woodland birds and bats are highly adapted to nesting or even hibernating in the tree-holes which would have existed in the numerous ancient trees. What could be more secure? Indeed it is only this adaptation which explains the fact that the female blue tit, great tit and nuthatch are as brightly coloured as the male, as they run no risk of attracting predators while sitting on a nest in a hole. But old trees with holes in them are precisely some of the things that are lacking in the typical secondary woodland, whether conifers or hardwoods, because the tree crop is harvested at between 50 and 150 years of age. This is the real reason why nest-boxes are so successful. We are only restoring to woodland one of the features to which our native species are adapted. The criticism that conservation is a purely artificial activity must be seen in this light. Man makes the woods artificial for his own purposes, and it is a short-coming not to make these artificial secondary woods imitate nature more closely. This seems a reasonable way of conserving our native species, and in the remaining chapters in this section we shall look at as many such methods as possible, which the ranger can carry out on his own area.

An idea which has not been tried extensively is the erection of boxes for birds of prey, especially the long-eared owl, in extensive young plantations, as the chief limitation for them in this situation may well be nest-sites.

Detailed notes on nestboxes and batboxes are given in the 3 following illustration pages.

Pair of redstarts investigating nestbox on mature Scots pine

Nestboxes (1)

Site

a) Away from areas where human vandalism or interference likely. Best by forest houses or remote from paths in the forest. Otherwise all boxes should be positioned over 3 m from the ground, and best not to number boxes on outside.

b) Away from preferred natural sites, eg old hardwoods. Best sites in typical FC woods are in mature (30+ years) conifers (especially by clearings, grassy rides, field edges, pools, etc.). This allows species to forage in conifer plantations while nesting in their chosen habitat, eg pied flycatchers in an oak belt. As a result boxes may be sited fairly densely (15 per hectare +).

Position on tree

a) Height: 1.5 to 4.5 m normally. Consider human interference, and maximum safe height you can work on your ladder.

b) Not facing prevailing wind (usually SW) nor due south if sunshine falls heavily on box, ie usually north to south east.

c) With nestbox entrance tilted downwards whether in side or (as illustrated) front of box

d) Away from water courses on tree trunk.

e) Away from very close branches which predators could use. For the same reason perches should not be put on the box. (Chief predators of nest-boxes are Man, weasels, greater spotted woodpecker and squirrels). Metal hole-plates (obtainable from RSPB) and well-built boxes are further deterrents. On the other hand some species like nearby perches and the final approach should not be too much in the open.

Maintenance and inspection

a) Boxes should be visited in late winter (February - March) for replacement and repair. Also clean out old nests and eggs but don't dislodge nests of small rodents, especially dormice, unless certainly disused.

b) A useful kit can be prepared for nestbox-visiting: aluminium ladder, notebook, small pliers, small coil of wire, or spare hooks, impact glue or woodfiller, inner tube strips (both as roof-fasteners and repair clamps), spare roof felt, penknife, etc

c) Fastenings to the tree must be loosened periodically to allow for growth.

d) Boxes may be oiled periodically, but not treated with creosote or other wood preservatives.

e) Loose boxes must be taken down as they are dangerous to you. You should not visit boxes on your own if you are climbing a ladder, and a safety helmet should be worn!

It is not an offence to visit nest-boxes without written permission (as it is for bats) unless you find a schedule 1 species (eg wryneck) in residence, in which case leave it strictly alone. See 'Ranger and the law'. Do not disturb boxes unnecessarily during nest-making, hatching and just before young are due to fly. Do not risk breaking eggs, which are often hidden in the bedding. Leave nuthatches alone for fear of dislodging mud inside the box onto the nest. Bird-ringing may only be undertaken by licence from the countryside agencies.

The ranger worth his salt will usually prefer to watch the box to see what species is using it.

Nestboxes (2)

Design

a) Useful materials are 20 25 mm rough sawn planks, 10 mm seasoned planks, or marine ply (BS 1088). Boxes may be cut with ease from planks (see diagrams).

b) Grain of wood should run up and down box (especially roof) not to side. Roofing felt on the lid is a great advantage. The lid should overhang the entrance hole.

c) Boxes must have drainage holes in floor (5 mm diameter).

d) Boxes should be openable for cleaning and inspection, but the lids must fasten securely, usually with a hook and eye on each side, to avoid predator interference. Strips cut from inner tubes can provide alternative security (illustrated previous page).

e) To avoid water running in down the back of the box, roofs can hinge with a strip of inner tube or (as illustrated on previous page) have a batten over the top of the join between roof and back.

f) The roof is kept snugly in place by an internal batten fitting the inside of the box.

g) Species are selected by the design of box and also hole diameter eg less than 38 mm to exclude starlings, less than 32 mm to exclude house sparrows, so that 29 mm is popular.

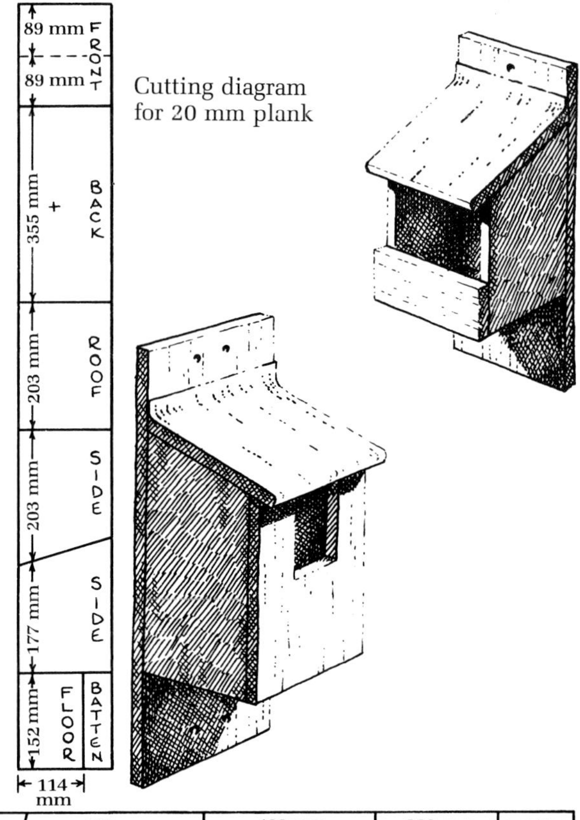

Cutting diagram for 20 mm plank

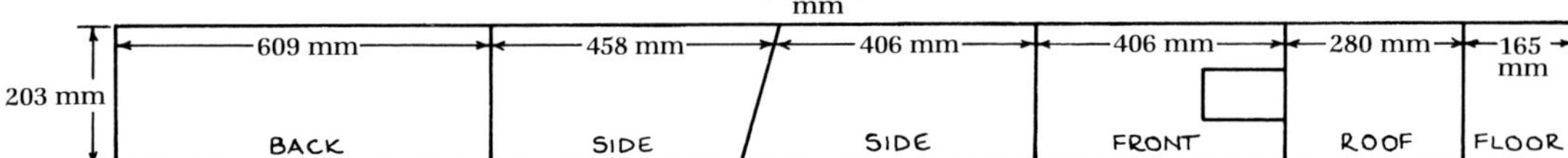

The small box may be built for hole nesters (as illustrated on previous page) or open fronted (above) in which case only 90 mm front. Species: (hole-nester) tits, redstart, pied flycatcher, tree sparrow, starling, wren, greater spotted woodpecker, wryneck, nuthatch, treecreeper. Species: (open-front) spotted flycatcher, robin, pied & grey wagtails, redstart, wren, dipper.

The large box could also be built with a 460 mm back and mounted on a 600 mm batten. The entrance hole is 100 mm wide by 150 mm deep. Species: little owl, jackdaw, greater spotted woodpecker, stock dove. A slightly larger version (especially with wider sides cut from a bigger piece of wood) would also attract kestrels, tawny owl and hole nesting ducks.

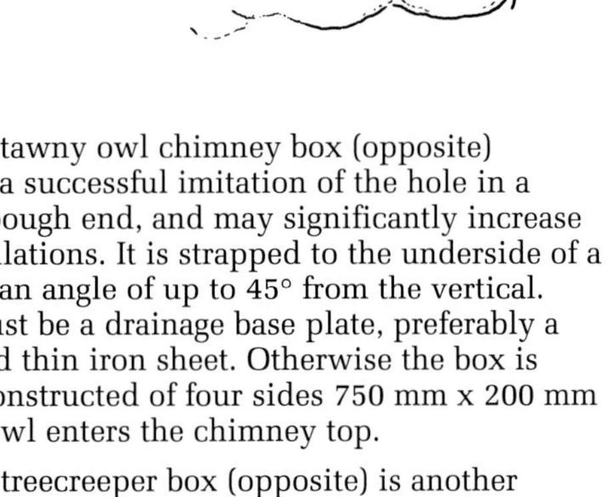

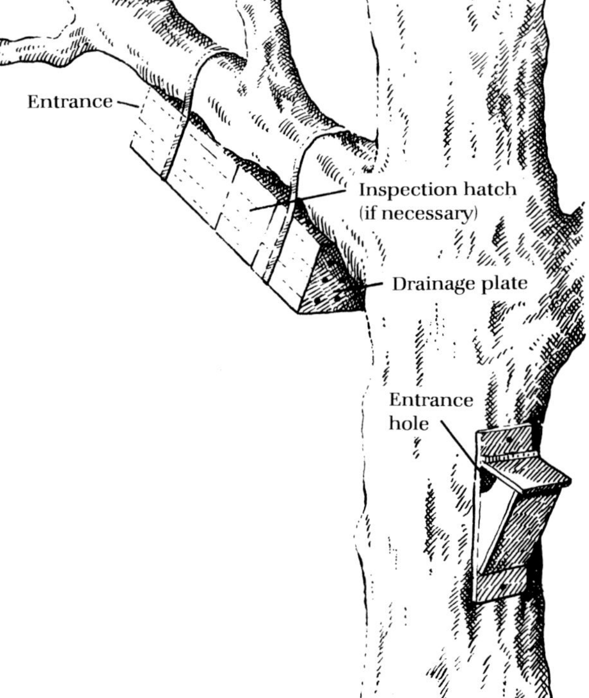

The tawny owl chimney box (opposite) provides a successful imitation of the hole in a broken bough end, and may significantly increase owl populations. It is strapped to the underside of a bough at an angle of up to 45° from the vertical. There must be a drainage base plate, preferably a perforated thin iron sheet. Otherwise the box is simply constructed of four sides 750 mm x 200 mm and the owl enters the chimney top.

The treecreeper box (opposite) is another proven success in its imitation of a natural site – the crevice of bark on an old tree.

These two examples illustrate the fact that the design of nestboxes is only the product of imagination and the understanding of the requirements of a species.

Further reference may be made to the BTO field guide to nestboxes.

Bat conservation

Cross section of roosting box

Roofing felt layer

Removable lid

152 mm

190 mm

458 mm

140 mm

Roosting boxes may be made from unplaned planks 150 mm wide and at least 25 mm thick. The boxes may be made taller for large species, but should not be wider

Entry slit 13–20 mm. At least 50 mm wide

Small saw cuts may be provided in smooth timber

Alternative position of entry slit

Box attached by copper nails and/or straps not ferrous nails

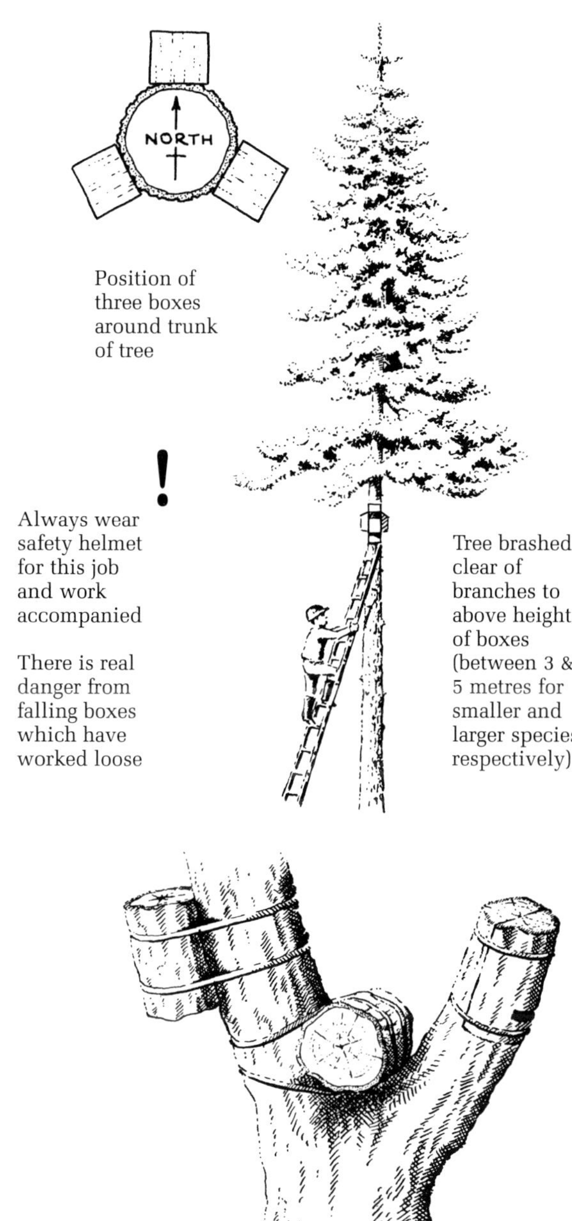

Some possible designs for hibernation boxes of which the essential features are strong holding straps, and a narrow slit leading up to a small, well-insulated chamber (at least 100 mm of wood all round)

British bats have been on the decline in recent years and a number of factors are implicated: loss of habitat in old woodland, suitable buildings, and caves (made worse by disturbance from potholing); the increased use of timber preservatives in roof timbers, and of insecticides generally; also mishandling by naturalists.

Probably the most positive step that can therefore be taken in a Forestry Commission context (in addition to general forest design and habitat improvement) is the provision of bat-boxes in plantations lacking natural sites.

Roosting boxes are sited in a group of up to 60 boxes (3 per tree 20 trees) scattered over an area of about one hectare. The best sites are adjacent to field edges (especially grass), rides, clearings and pools and well away from natural or existing sites (eg old hardwoods) and any possible interference. Such a site could be left to mature beyond the normal rotation.

Long-eared bat

1) Position of testes in males, visible from upper side, an aid to ageing

2) Position of nipples in adult females, these provide a good indication of maturity as surrounding hair has been worn by previous suckling

Hibernation boxes are equally valuable, but need to be constructed to provide a high degree of insulation. Under no circumstances should bats or boxes be disturbed or handled during the months November–March inclusive, as this may cause bats to expend fat reserves essential to survival through the winter.

At least one annual inspection of boxes and contents should be made each summer, in relation to which see details of legal protection afforded to bats in Section 7D.

Don't handle bats unnecessarily or carelessly.

F. Reptile conservation areas

A den of adders in March

Snakes and lizards form another group of species which may be conserved successfully in secondary woodland. The presence of one of the two nationally rare species (smooth snake and sand lizard) calls for the creation of a conservation area beyond any shadow of doubt. But all British reptiles should be considered as animals which cannot adapt to unsuitable habitats, and probably all six species (the two above plus adder, grass snake, slow worm and common lizard) are in decline. This is because in Great Britain they are at the edge of their natural range, and limited by poor powers of dispersal as well as a decrease in suitable habitat.

Male grass snake. Note yellow colour

Where reptiles are found in the forest, it will be because there exists a warm micro-climate, available shelter from predators (including Man), adequate food supply, and appropriate wintering quarters. The ranger who is familiar with his beat will probably already know locations where, for example, adders are to be seen when they emerge from hibernation in early spring. It may be that suitable conditions are found so widely in the forest that conservation would be pointless. But more commonly, the reptiles will be restricted to a few small areas of the forest, or (as often happens in new plantations) an apparently healthy population is about to be shaded out of existence altogether by growing trees, usually after a brief period of increased numbers of reptiles on the forest edge. In these instances the creation of reptile conservation areas is appropriate. Management involves:

- Choosing an area inside the forest with a good existing population of reptiles, and leaving a small site aside from the shading effect of the normal forest rotation. Maintain this site clear of dense tree cover and encourage the development of a tussocky, grassy heathland or low scrub vegetation. A typically ideal site would be a south-facing gentle sunny slope with a number of ridges or terraces, especially running down towards a pool or stream (see illustration opposite). Some of the ridges and mounds can be cleared bare for basking areas. Old stumps and logs may be introduced for this purpose as well. Equally there should be some dense cover such as thorny scrub or overgrown deep plough furrows in which the reptiles may seek refuge from predators.
- Grass snakes may be encouraged further by providing a large pile of rotting vegetation, grass cuttings, manure and sawdust in a sunny and undisturbed site. They will use this to lay their eggs in around June to July, for hatching in August to September. Grass snakes in particular prefer a habitat closely associated with water, and are especially unwilling to tolerate disturbance.
- The conservation of the rare sand lizard is usually a matter for specialist attention, though it may be said that the essential measure is to preserve areas of deep exposed sand in sunny situations in which they lay their eggs.
- One form of normal forest management which could fit in well as part of a reptile conservation area is a Christmas tree plantation. Provided the trees are not grown beyond 2.5 m or so, rotational strips of young conifers provide good habitat for reptiles. If adders are present it is, of course, sensible to conduct planting, weeding and cutting operations with caution, if not indeed with chainsaw gloves on! Christmas tree plantations appear to suit the rare smooth snake particularly well, on the heathery areas this reptile favours.
- Sunny grass rides and internal forest road edges can be managed as extensions of a reptile conservation area, but only if they do not involve increased human disturbance of the conservation area.
- The essential characteristics of a reptile conservation area may be summarised as Seclusion, Sun and Scrub vegetation. Remember the 3S's for snakes!

Reptile and amphibian conservation area

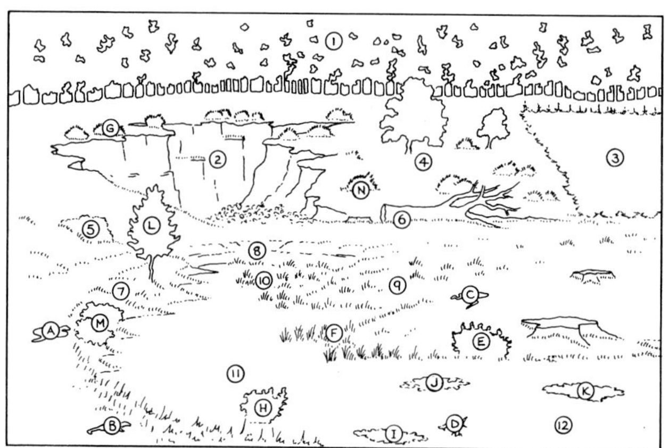

Habitats

1. Plantation edge.
2. Quarry of fissured rock face providing hibernation sites.
3. Christmas tree plantation.
4. Area of scrub, possibly with banks or deep plough furrows.
5. Heap of decaying vegetation for grass snake and slow-worm breeding site.
6. Stumps and lying dead tree for basking and shelter.
7. Rough scrubby vegetation on pool bank below open sandy ledge or dam top.
8. Sandy or shingly pool bank.
9. Rough grassy, tussocky area.
10. Shallow weedy water (up to 300 mm) for frog spawning.
11. Slightly deeper weedy water (up to 600 mm – 1 m) for toad spawning.
12. Deep water with plants suitable for newt breeding (600 mm – 2 m).

Reptile and amphibian species

A. Adder
B. Common lizard
C. Grass snake
D. Palmate newts

Plant species

E. Ragged robin
F. Soft rush
G. Gorse
H. Blue water speedwell
I. Common crowfoot
J. Starwort
K. Frogbit
L. Young birch tree
M. Bramble
N. Thorn bushes

G. Pools, wetlands, amphibians and dragonflies

i. Introducing pools and wetland habitats

Few rangers have beats which do not include streams, pools or marshy areas, and these are likely to be major sites for diversifying the habitat in the forest, one of our most important conservation aims. In the natural state before Man, wetlands were probably the second-most widespread habitat in Britain after woodland, and so there are innumerable species highly adapted to conditions in or near water. Some of these, such as the great crested newt, have already become uncommon as a result of the loss of habitat from drainage, pollution and disturbance. A well-managed forest pool or marsh with unpolluted water in an undisturbed part of the forest could easily be the best chance that some species have to survive, and later maybe to spread to other areas which are not so well protected at present.

We need first of all to know something about the habitats associated with water. The classification of streams, rivers, lakes and ponds depends principally upon their size, water temperatures during the year, speed of flow, liability to spate and on the type of rock over which they flow. These are the main determinants (other than Man's influence through pollution and disturbance) of the oxygen content, acidity, nutrient content and bottom composition, which in turn produce a certain type of vegetation and fish-life. Many of these factors are best measured by a freshwater biologist, and the ranger is well advised to contact the appropriate River Authority or River Purification Board in Scotland for analyses and tests before undertaking any major project.

On the margin between land and water, the following habitats occur:

Flooded areas on mineral soils are known as reed-swamps, and are invariably dominated by common reed *(Phragmites),* club rush *(Scirpus)* or reed mace *(Typha).* Club rush is the true bulrush, though most people associate this name with reed mace. These emergent plants form the transition stage between open water and marsh.

Waterlogged areas on mineral soils are known as marshes. Before being drained for agriculture, these once covered vast areas of lowland Britain, and have a very diverse flora, including such species as great willowherb, kingcup, meadowsweet, water mint, hemp-agrimony, ragged robin, marsh horsetail and several species of sedge. Marshes are usually in a state of succession from reed-swamp towards wet woodlands, a process which occurs when trees such as willow, alder and alder buckthorn invade open marsh.

Waterlogged areas on acid organic soils (in other words on peat) are known as bogs. Their vegetation includes such species as cottongrass and sphagnum moss.

Waterlogged areas on alkaline organic soils are known as fens. The whole habitat is now rare. It not only supports several marsh species, but also some distinctive plants of its own, such as fen violet and deptford pink, and rare insects such as the swallowtail butterfly. The existence of any fen on Forestry Commission land will certainly call for a conservation area.

ii. Planning a forest pool and surroundings

Before beginning to build a forest pool, there are a few important assessments and decisions to make:

- ***What is the existing habitat like?*** It would, for example, be a great mistake to destroy the entire length of a stream which has rare plants on its banks or in the area to be flooded. Such a situation might point towards creating a number of very small pools down the stream, or building the pool further up or downstream, or indeed, managing the streamside for its existing habitat and abandoning the idea of a pool.
- ***What is the pH value of the water?*** (pH is a measure of acidity–alkalinity in which 7 is neutral, values below 7 are increasingly acid and vice versa). Although there is little or nothing to be done about pH, its measure provides a baseline for pollution detection, as well as a pointer to the wildlife which can be expected in a pool and to the type of rocks over which the water flows. Many fish species, freshwater molluscs and crustaceans will not tolerate acidity, and, given a choice, it is often best to choose a more alkaline site. On the other hand dragonflies, for example, tend to favour more acidic pools if all else is suitable. Where possible, as always, the best solution is to choose more than one site to create the greatest possible diversity of habitat.
- ***Is the water supply too polluted to support wildlife?***
- ***What is the annual flow of water?*** In particular, what is the likely maximum flood flow, and what is the likely minimum drought flow? For a small pool it may be reasonable to rely on observation to decide whether the water flow is both reliable and safe. For larger pools there are specific calculations to be made and it is essential that the Forestry Commission Civil Engineers are involved.
- ***What are the legal requirements?*** Any new on-stream dam must be approved by the River Authority, or River Purification Board, and permission must be sought from both upstream and downstream landowners. The main relevant legislation is the 1973

Water Act, also the Salmon and Freshwater Fisheries Acts, 1923 and 1975.

● ***What is the best point on the stream for a pool?*** All other factors being equal, the answer will normally be where the surrounding banks are at their narrowest (for an on-stream dam) and in an area of the forest where the pool and its wildlife will not be unduly disturbed.

● ***What is the most appropriate way of constructing the pool?*** The usual method is to lay a pipe to carry the streamwater, and then dig the pool with an excavator and build the dam over the pipe. If the natural soil does not have a good clay content it will be necessary to bring in clay for the core of the dam before topping this with excavated soil.

But, would an off-stream pool be preferable to this normal on-stream design? The advantage of off-stream pools are that they do not require notification of the River Authorities/River Purification Board, they may be sited wherever required and the water level may be regulated easily. For this last reason, off-stream systems are particularly useful for creating and maintaining an area of marsh, reed-swamp or very shallow water. It is even possible to construct such a pool by embanking above ground level, whereas this method is inadvisable for an on-stream pool, for which a cardinal rule is to keep the length of a dam and embankment to a minimum. Experience suggests that for forest pools off-stream designs are often best.

These methods will, of course, only work where there is an impermeable soil, a high water table or sufficiently strong water supply to counteract drainage. Otherwise it will be necessary to construct a pond with an artificial bottom of clay, buried polythene or concrete. Such ponds may also be constructed without a stream supply, in which case they are known as dew ponds. These rely on surface run-off as well as direct rainfall, and so should be constructed with as large an area of the surrounds sloping into the pond as possible.

When contemplating the creation of a pool it is of paramount importance to ensure that there will be sufficient water available throughout the year. There is no point in creating a pool for frogs which dries up before the tadpoles have completed their metamorphosis.

Successful pools have been created, especially in peat with an underlying clay soil, by blasting with explosive.

● ***How is the water level to be controlled?*** It is obviously essential for every pool to have a main outflow, and it is useful if this can be regulated. Anything other than a small pool should in addition have a spillway or storm overflow to cope with the maximum possible volume of floodwater produced by the stream. It is important that this overflow is constructed with material which cannot erode in such a flood. Bags filled with a sand and cement mix are good for this purpose.

The pool in the colour illustration (overleaf) has been constructed in the original stream-bed, but has been partly converted to an off-stream pool by adding a channel before the stream enters the pool, thereby regulating the amount of water going through the pool. The normal outflow has been constructed by adding an elbow and vertical pipes to the drain, running under the dam, which was used during construction. These pipes can now be removed again to enable total drainage of the pool, if necessary, at a later date. There are several methods of designing a pool, but in all cases the safety margin for coping with floodwater should be generous.

● ***How is maintenance work going to be carried out after the pool is constructed?*** Especially in a large pool, some forethought should be applied to the problems which will arise from the natural tendency of all pools to silt up. Firstly, there should be a silt-trap (as illustrated) before the stream enters the pool, which will require regular cleaning. Part of the illustrated silt-trap is a self-emptying device. Secondly, there should be access for heavy machinery on solid ground. This is particularly useful near the top end of the pool for dredging silt, and near any other shallow, marshy areas whose vegetation will cause a slow succession towards dry land conditions. Thirdly, it is a good idea to position the storm outflow on the downwind edge of the pool so that leaves will tend to be driven to this corner, where they may then be flushed or raked clear. The last resort in silting up is to drain a pool entirely. Because of the damage to wildlife that this causes, draining should be seen as a last resort, but it is useful to include the facility to drain the pool in its design.

iii. Designing a forest pool for wildlife

Whether designing a new pool or improving an old one, it is usually an advantage to have varied surrounds, shoreline and depth to the pool. This means creating as many of the following habitat features as possible.

● An area of adjoining waterlogged vegetation (marsh, bog or fen, according to the locality), which is as important as the pool itself in terms of the variety of wildlife which will be attracted to the site, especially as this feature is often overlooked. At least one side of the pool should, therefore, slope very gently from shallow water up to a flat marshy area. It is a considerable advantage to be able to control the water supply to a marsh by means of the sluice, as shown in the illustration.

● It is equally important, when digging or

Wildlife pool management

Representation of a medium sized (½-1 hectare) wildlife pond

1. Varied surroundings to pond and seclusion from disturbance. (Some large trees in vicinity).
2. Dead tree for heron perch.
3. Fluted edges for wildfowl and amphibians – gentle slopes for ducklings.
4. Each bay approximately 2.5 m wide and 4 m inland. Less than 150 mm deep to deter pike.
5. Sandy cliff for kingfishers and sand martins.
6. Overhanging vegetation provides fish food.
7. Storm channel positioned so prevailing wind blows leaves on water surface to this corner for cleaning.
8. Dam.
9. Primary outlet and drainage pipe in deep water near dam to ensure circulation in pool is good.
10. Island with alder, willow as overstorey and broom, gorse or dogwood as ground cover. Fluted edges as on poolside.
11. Shingle beach for breeding shoreline birds.
12. Deep water areas for overwintering fish.
13. Signboard to read 'No fishing upstream of this point' – restrict any fishing to part of pool and banks.
14. Reedside fringe and shallows with rooted and emergent vegetation (best near head of pond).
15. Marsh.
16. Sluice to overflow channel and silt traps.
17. Bed of entering stream.
18. Overflow channel rejoins stream downstream or feeds another marsh.
19. Sluice into marsh.
20. Hard access for heavy machinery to work on marsh and pool.

Plant Species

A. Willowherb
B. Horsetails
C. Kingcups
D. Ragged robin
E. Rushes and sedges
F. Reeds and reedmace
G. Yellow flag
H. Broad leaved pondweed and water lilies
I. Water millfoil
J. Floating vegetation frogbit and duckweeds
K. Soft rush

Outlet

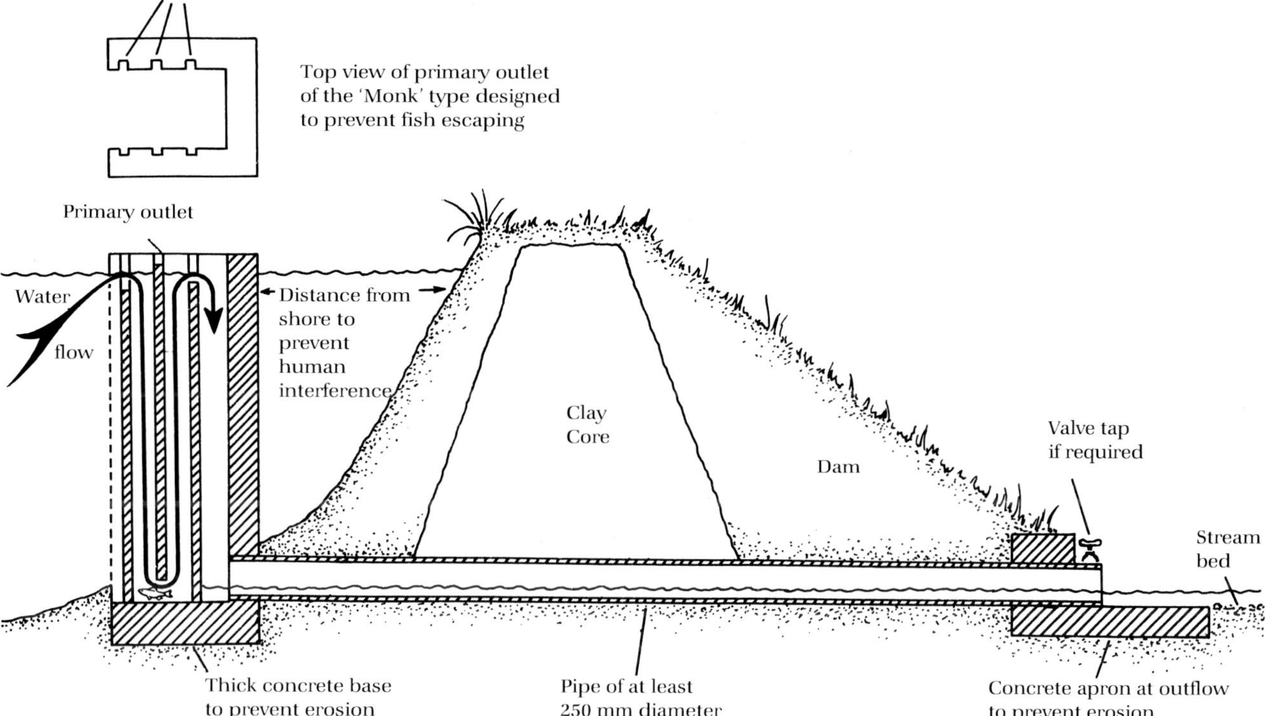

Inlet

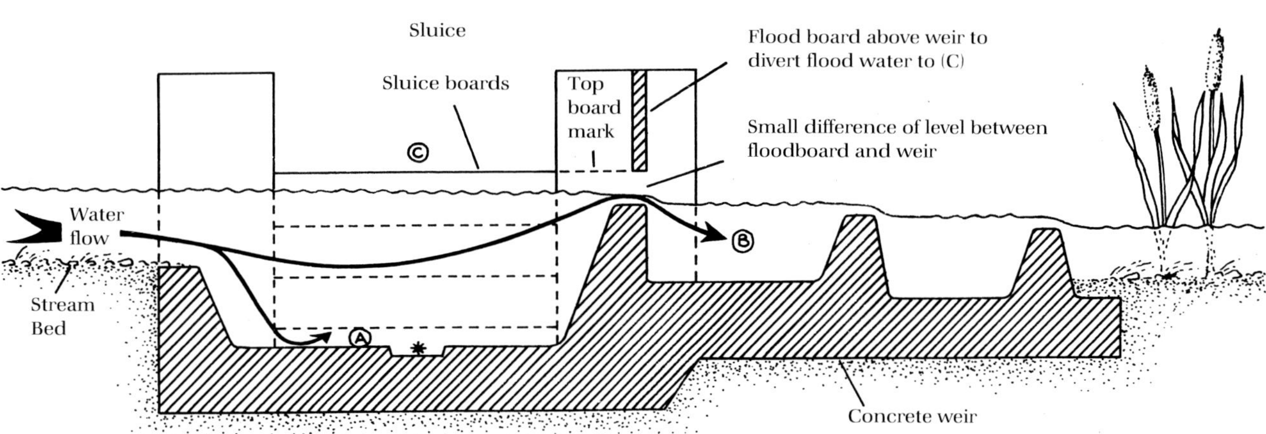

In very dry weather it may be necessary to slide the sluice boards right down leaving only the slight gap in the silt trap base (✱) open

Water flows normally (A) under sluice boards so that this area is a self-emptying silt trap and (B) into pool via concrete weir which may be emptied of silt with a shovel. In very wet weather water may also flow over (C) the top sluice board which is just above the level of the concrete weir

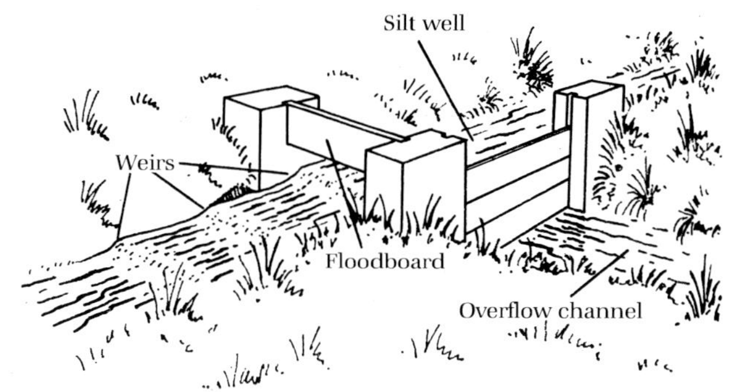

dredging, not to make a steeply sloping bottom to the pool itself on all sides. If there is a large shelf just below the intended water-line on one side then shallow-water vegetation, especially reed-swamp, can become established. Like marshland, this is one of the most important habitats for wildlife. Reeds offer rich feeding areas to waterfowl (because they act as a seed trap) as well as breeding sites for reed and sedge warblers, grebes, bearded reedlings and emergent insects, such as dragonflies which have declined dramatically in recent years. A large area of reed-swamp is particularly useful as a delta near the entrance to a pool, where it acts as a natural silt-trap.

● The shoreline should not run in a straight edge, but be as wavy and indented as possible, as this increases the amount of water-edge habitat, and provides species which live in this zone with the necessary shelter, especially on a large pool. Wildfowl will be amongst those species to benefit as the number of their breeding territories increases if the individual pairs are not always in line of sight of one another. The sketch in Section 6 C gives details of a brood-bay for ducks. Remember to have a length of gentle slope in such bays to enable ducklings to clamber out of the pool.

● Although it is important not to have an abrupt transition from dry land to water on all sides, it is useful in a fish-pool to have one length of fairly steep bank with vegetation and trees overhanging the water, as these provide food in the form of insects which drop into the water. Where fish are present there needs to be an area of deep water (2 m - 4 m) to provide them with an over-wintering area. The deepest part of the pool should be near the main outflow in order to maintain water circulation. Further details in relation to fish and wildfowl are given in Section 6.

● If the soil is fairly sandy and stone-free, a length of bare vertical bank will provide a site for both kingfishers and sand martins to nest. This may need to be maintained by cutting the bank (faces should be at least 1.5 m high), trimming back excess vegetation on the face or even building up and consolidating new faces, as these species will not nest once the bank has slumped or become overgrown.

● An island greatly enhances a pool by providing extra protection, especially for shore-nesting birds which are otherwise vulnerable to foxes as well as human disturbances. A large area hollowed out in the middle of the island and filled with sand and shingle is ideal for such birds, and the island is also a good place to try a nestbox suitable for wagtails.

iv. Amphibians and dragonflies

The seclusion of forest pools is especially suitable for the conservation of amphibians, which are in decline in Britain for much the same reasons as reptiles, while also suffering heavy losses from people collecting spawn and newts. Adult amphibians (frogs, toads and newts) spend much of the non-breeding season distributed through warm, moist and food-rich habitats, eg woodland vegetation, hedge bottoms, grassland, gardens, pool edges and under stones. Nonetheless, their ability to reproduce depends upon the availability of suitable breeding ponds and juvenile newts often remain in the tadpole stage during their first winter.

Frogs breed in shallow, weedy water, up to 300 mm or more deep, in a warm site, often the north (south facing) edge of a pool, or even just in a ditch or dewpond with a reliable water level. The run-offs made by the Forestry Commission engineers beside forest roads have been known to serve as frog pools, provided they are dug in an impermeable soil which holds some water well into the summer.

Toads also select warm and weedy sites, but in water up to 1 m deep. The rare natterjack toad, however, breeds in very shallow and warm water, often with little weed growth; conditions which are usually found in association with coastal dunes and sandy heaths. The presence of natterjacks would call for very careful conservation measures.

Newts breed in deeper water (600 mm - 2 m) which will support submerged and floating vegetation on whose leaves they lay their eggs (water crowfoot and water startwort are known favourites). The presence of the rare great crested newt would greatly enhance the value of a conservation pool.

The conservation of amphibians is probably best carried out by means of relatively small forest pools where predation by wildfowl and particularly fish is minimised. If a large pool is intended, it will be a good idea to build some small pools and ditches to one side for amphibians, or make a few bays protected from the main pool by a lip near the surface of the water.

Dragonflies also favour conditions where fish and wildfowl are not numerous, and it may well be more worthwile, from a conservation view point, designing a pool for amphibians and dragonflies rather than the obvious solution of fish and duck. Detailed notes on the further requirements of dragonflies may be found in the Nature Conservancy Council publication *The Conservation of Dragonflies.* Warm, shallow pools which are not overshaded are prefered, especially surrounded by scrubby vegetation and rides leading through the trees to other open areas. But the pool should never be deprived of all surrounding shelter so forest glades which act as sun-traps are ideal.

Even firepools can serve as amphibian conservation areas, provided that frogs, toads and newts can climb out of them, and, if necessary, a few pieces of wood may be left trailing from the edge into the firepool for this purpose.

v. Pool maintenance and protection

Pools and wetlands almost invariably require maintenance to prevent them reverting towards dry-land conditions.

● Remember to clean silt traps regularly, and rake leaves and debris from all sluices.

● All major maintenance work should be carried out in the autumn months, to minimise harm to wildlife. This includes dredging and dragging marshland and uprooting unwanted invasive tree species, as well as dredging pools to remove silt. It is obviously preferable when using heavy machinery to tackle only half of a given habitat in one year, and leave the other half undisturbed for its wildlife.

● If weed control is a problem in the pool, cutting and digging by heavy machinery, by hand or by chain-scythe is preferable to chemical control in all cases where wildlife is a consideration.

● Where chemical weed control and insect control is taking place in the forest, the surrounds and watersheds to forest pools and streams should be left unsprayed, especially where these drain into water supplies. Such non-spray watersheds should be marked by the ranger on the wildlife map.

● It is Forestry Commission policy that chemical spraying equipment should not be rinsed out in firepools and forest pools. The ranger should ensure that the forest staff is strongly advised that all such equipment is carried to the properly designed washing bays at forest depots.

H. Heath and moorland

i. Introducing heath and moorland habitats

Forestry Commission woods have been and are being planted on former heath and moorland as extensively as on any habitat. Many heaths and moors were originally created, and are still maintained by Man's activities, but they are some of the last refuges for several of our native species, such as the golden plover, dunlin, merlin, red-backed shrike and sand lizard. Heathland in particular is one of the most valuable conservation assets, as it is a habitat whose worldwide distributions is restricted to Britain and the north-west European coast. Unfortunately large areas of heath (and to a lesser extent moorland) have been destroyed in recent years.

The difference between heath and moor is that true moorland has a thick layer of bog-peat resulting from the prevention of normal decomposition by waterlogging; whereas on heaths, decomposition is prevented by the free draining soil beneath, producing a thinner dry-peat layer. In both heath and moor, however, the extreme acidity of peat soil and the high coastal or upland exposure, plus usually fire or grazing management, combine to prevent normal tree growth. Instead the dominant vegetation is composed of dwarf evergreen shrubs (many of the heather family) and other plants adapted to conditions of high exposure. For example the cottony flowering heads of the cottongrasses are known to reduce the effects of drastic temperature change to which exposed sites are prone. Gorse, broom, juniper and heathers are adapted to survive exposure by the modification of their leaves to reduce transpiration.

Heathland plants

Dry heathland plants

● On dry lowland heaths, common heather (=ling) associates predominantly with bell-heather and bracken. In places gorse, broom, hawthorn, brambles, briars and honeysuckle may form dense clumps of scrub heath, or succession towards birch and pine woodland may be taking place. Where heath or moor verges on acid grassland, wavy hair grass, purple moor grass, mat grass, tormentil, heath bedstraw and sheep sorrel (host of the small copper butterfly) are usually common.

● On moorland (=heather moor), common heather, purple moor grass, cross-leaved heath, crowberry, bilberry and (on banks and ledges) hard fern are major constituents of the vegetation. Bilberry moor may become particularly dominant at high altitudes, and also in the shade where a moorland vegetation underlies an old pine or oak wood. (As with acid grassland, this is a reminder how in reality the different habitats merge into one another).

As the peat becomes wetter and thicker deer grass and cotton grass become dominant. Cottongrasses are sedge-related plants which are the hosts to the large heath butterfly. In the very wettest situation, known as blanket bog, sphagnum mosses and lichens make up the dominant plant life.

ii. Species of particular conservation value

As in woodland, the ranger should look for species of rarity and particular conservation significance when surveying and assessing an area of heath and moor. It is important that forest design areas and the best conservation sites are marked on the wildlife map and left unplanted within the forest fence.

The 'leks' of black grouse are entirely traditional sites on which these birds gather from an area of several square miles in order to display and mate. The ranger should identify leks by observation from March onward, and they should not be planted up on Forestry Commission land. As Fraser Darling wrote of this species, "here is a highly organised social system in being alongside our own but one which has developed quite independently of us ...., with Man observing in part, but not comprehending". These words would hold true for all other traditional species, such as the badger, which we should attempt to conserve.

It would be helpful if we also knew how to make allowances for such traditional moorland-nesters as golden plover, greenshank and dunlin. As golden plover nest in fairly dense colonies, it might be thought an easy plan would be to conserve them by leaving a

Wet moorland plants

chosen site unplanted. Unfortunately this would be unlikely to work in isolation, that is to say unless accompanied by an extensive area (probably several hundred hectares) of their favoured habitat of moorland bog and lochans mixed together. It is thought that these traditional moorland species (and others such as ring ouzel, hen harrier) will not return on to re-stock areas.

Similarly, the survival of many of our rarer lowland heath species (such as the Dartford warbler and silver-studded blue butterfly) also depend upon extensive areas of suitable habitat. In both these cases, therefore, at least a part of such moorland or heathland habitat should be conserved on Forestry Commission land if it is adjacent to other extensive holdings in, for example, private or County Council ownership. (In the unusual situation of land-use at the New Forest, the Commission is solving these problems entirely on its own land).

Just as margins of natural vegetation are being left unplanted beside streams, as part of forest design, so areas are left unplanted around moorland lochans. This will allow these lochans to be used by such unusual species as the red-throated diver.

It will be very worthwhile leaving selected sites of moorland, bog and heath where any unusual flora exists. In this respect the ranger can keep an eye open for bog rosemary *(Andromeda polifolia),* ivy-leaved bellflower *(Wahlenbergia hederacea),* lesser skullcap *(Scutellaria minor),* which are all national rarities. Also such interesting plants as the butterworts *(Pinguicula spp),* sundews *(Drosera spp),* common cowheat *(Melampyrum pratense),* heath spotted orchid *(Dactylorhiza maculata),* clubmosses *(Tycopidium spp).*

Golden plover

iii. Management

The aim of managing heath or moorland for conservation is to retain the maximum diversity of plant communities and habitats, particularly in relation to the age of the heather. The heather cycle often lasts as long as 50 years after burning, during which time several different stages of vegetation are represented before reversion to scrub and woodland begins to take place. Management of heath or moorland for conservation therefore calls for far less frequent burning than is required for sheep or grouse alone. Burning should also only be carried out on sections at a time, so that the ideal conservation heath or moorland will become a mosaic of different plant communities, including scrub and bog.

On some areas even the most occasional burning may be impractical.

Dunlin

Reversion to scrub may then be prevented by the use of a heavy swipe on the back of a tractor. In small sites (particularly rides), birch and other invasive species may be controlled by means of a clearing-saw. Limited grazing also has a part to play in creating heathland diversity. Limited grazing and burning combined with heather cutting will create a more diverse heathland and moorland than burning alone, which encourages bracken invasion in lowland areas especially.

From the conservation viewpoint, burning is definitely not desirable in the management of wet peat-bog areas of upland moor. The main points of management for these areas is to prevent burning and drainage taking place.

Some of the best conservation areas in upland forest are open woodlands (pine, birch, oak, rowan, holly, willow) with upland moorland vegetation and woodland vegetation combined underneath. These are often self-maintaining if used as deer-glades, and again burning should clearly not take place.

Greenshank

I. Traditional species (badgers, eagles, etc.)

For some animals it is not enough to preserve their general habitat, because they are traditional in some aspect of their social lives as well. Badger setts are often hundreds of years old, and a group of badgers disturbed from their home cannot re-establish themselves in the way that, for example, a solitary sow and cubs will. The major badger setts of an areas should be noted in the wildlife plan, and the immediate surrounds to the sett left undisturbed by forestry operations, including felling. This involves the loss of a half to one hectare of timber, and creates a conservation area with several points of interest.

An important point in the protection of badgers is not to publicise the whereabouts of their setts, as (especially in the north Midlands) there is still a great deal of illegal badger-digging. (Equally well the best policy with the nests of birds of prey is to avoid drawing attention to their whereabouts and existence, because of illegal nest-robbing by people making money from the falconry trade). Pesticides may also be partly responsible for the evident decline of the badger in some areas.

Where rabbit-fencing is placed across runs, it is usually necessary to construct badger-gates, as detailed in Forestry Commission Leaflet 68 and Bulletin 102.

Two other members of the mustelid family, the pine marten and the otter, also appear to be fairly conservative in the use of their dens and holts. Though marten dens are usually less easily recognised than badger setts, they should be left undisturbed once found (see Forestry Commission Forest Record 64). The main requirements of otters would seem to be for stretches of unpolluted waterways without excessive human disturbance.

Planting should be kept well clear of cliffs which contain special plant communities or the traditional nesting sites of such species as eagles and peregrines, otherwise these sites may be ruined as the plantations mature.

Badger

J. Grass rides and verges

Grassy areas (typically rides, verges, deer glades and amenity areas) add considerable diversification of habitat to the forest. They provide both grassland and woodland edge conditions which are excellent for reptiles, hedgehogs, deer, bats and butterflies such as the speckled wood and small skipper, whose food plants are grasses.

There is one other interesting point that the ranger should keep his eyes open for. Since the widespread destruction of old pasture in meadows, woodland rides have become some of the last reserves of unimproved grassland. Some rides and verges contain quite rare, poor colonising species, and a number of these are listed beneath. Several of them are very similar in habit to ancient woodland plants, but can tolerate less shaded conditions. Grassland and its associated species are usually classified according to degree of acidity/alkalinity of soil and dry/waterlogged nature of site.

More conservative species found on forest rides and edges include: adder's tongue *(Ophioglossum vulgatum)*; rock-rose *(Helianthemum nummularium)* the food plant of the brown argus butterfly larva; yellowwort *(Blackstonia perfoliata)*; clustered bellflower *(Campanula glomerata);* saw-wort *(Serratula tinctoria)*; great burnet *(Sanguisorba officialis)*; smooth tare *(Vicia tetrasperma);* Dyer's greenweed *(Genista tinctoria);* wild liquorice *(Astragalus glycyphyllos);* wood betony *(Betonica officinalis);* lady's-smock *(Cardamine pratense)*; cowslip *(Primula veris)*; common St.John's wort *(Hypericum perfoliatum)*; ragged robin *(Lychnis flos-cuculi)*; devil's-bit scabious *(Succisa pratensis)*; wild basil *(Clinipodium vulgare)*; wild marjoram *(Origanum vulgare)*; and any orchid species. Some of the above species are associated with damp grassland verging on to marshy wetland.

The management of woodland grass rides is best achieved by mowing at least once every two years, preferably fairly late in the season if one of the management aims is to allow flowering plants to develop in the sward. For deer management some rides may usefully be swiped twice annually. An outside strip should be left which is swiped every 3 or more years to create a woodland edge. This provides good diversification of habitat as well as (where applicable) browse species for deer. On the best rides in the forest it may also be desirable to cut back overshadowing trees as the forest crop develops.

Ride edge management for wildlife conservation

K. Insects and other invertebrates

Ideally, the conservation of invertebrates should be based upon a species list for each site in the forest, as with birds and mammals. As this is rarely possible in practice, the best way to conserve invertebrates is to conserve and develop as many as possible of the ancient or significant habitats already discussed - heathland, grassland, marshland, ancient trees, coppice woodland and so forth.

Most invertebrates rely upon very particular conditions, such as a combination of food plants and hosts, or a micro-habitat as specialised as the nesting materials accumulated in the heart of an old rotting tree. It follows that the gradual development or expansion of a significant site is usually better than drastic change, even if this change is in the direction of traditional management.

On the other hand, where the existing habitats in a wood are not significant, it should be possible to develop sites of value. Even the odd corner of scrub and verge of woodland edge vegetation can have considerable value to insects, and should be marked on the wildlife map as areas not to be chemically sprayed. Scrub vegetation is managed like the fringes of a woodland ride, by swiping only a portion of the area each year, in order to build up a mixed age structure of plants.

Several Forestry Commission woods are managed as important reserves for butterflies. Here the primary consideration is to maintain those habitats which support the food-plants of the caterpillars of the various species. A butterfly conservation area is illustrated overleaf, followed by a list of food-plants and habitats. Reference may also be made to the list of insects associated with British trees and shrubs, which is included in Section 2 B. But remember that quantity is not always better than quality!

For further reference, consult the useful book *Habitat Management for Invertebrates* by Peter Kirby (RSPB, 1992).

Rangers with an interest in the study of insects will find that running a moth trap is a rewarding long-term project, though this must not be one of the traps which kills the moths it catches, and the trap must be inspected after any night that it has been in use. Fibre egg-boxes placed in the trap allow the moths to pass the night comfortably.

Butterfly conservation

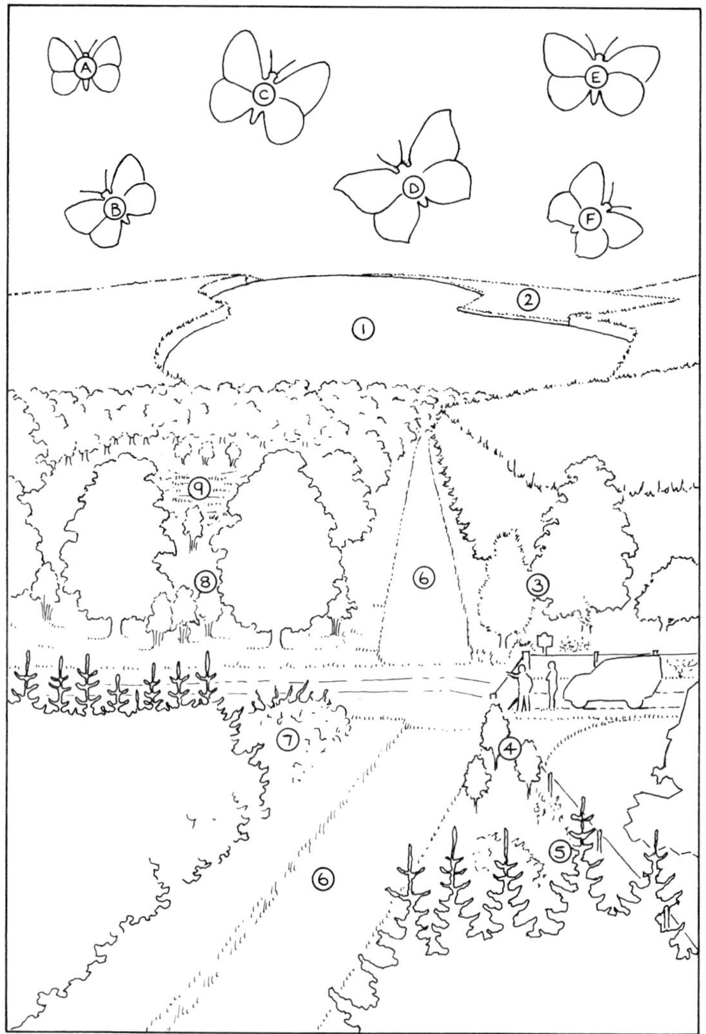

Habitats and plant species

1. Area of old heath, moor or down left unplanted.
2. Young planted stage mimics heath, moor, scrub and open woodland.
3. Wood edge and ride side: wych elm, holly, goat willow, hedge garlic, wild hop, ivy and blackthorn.
4. Amenity planting: alder buckthorn.
5. Field boundary: nettles, teasel and large bittercress.
6. Broad sunny woodland rides with strips on outside or down one half cut in alternative years provides: sunshine and shelter, mature woodland grass species, cropped grassland, and biennial flowers for larvae and adults. Long grass contains: wood vetch, bush vetch and meadow vetchling, hogweed and angelica, and wood millet. Short grass contains: birdsfoot trefoil, rock rose, violets and self heal.
7. Odd unused corners for scrub, eg bramble and blackthorn. NB Do not spray with insecticide.
8. Coppice-with-standards provides: ideal open woodland conditions – mature hardwood canopy (eg oak and elm); shrub species (eg hazel and honeysuckle); ground flora (eg violets, primroses and wood millet).
9. Secluded and sunny woodland clearing with marsh.

Butterfly species

A. Holly blue (female)
B. Green hairstreak (female)
C. Speckled wood (male)
D. Brimstone (female)
E. Small pearl-bordered fritillary (male)
F. Purple hairstreak (female)

Butterfly food-plants and habitats

In the brackets 'M' indicates migrant species which may breed in this country, in which case food-plant given, but does not overwinter. The asterisks indicate the more uncommon species: one asterisk is a species particularly worth conserving by habitat preservation, 2 asterisks indicate a nationally rare species whose habitat should never be destroyed. Indeed if followed by a 'P' these species and their habitats are protected by law.

Browns	Speckled wood	Grasses esp couch	Woodland
	Wall	Grasses	Wood-edges etc
	Mountain ringlet (**)	Grasses esp *Desch. caesp*	Upland conifer woods
	Scotch argus (*)	Grasses esp *Molinia,* couch	Upland conifer woods
	Marbled white (*)	Grasses	Grassy places
	Grayling	Grasses	Heaths, coasts
	Hedge brown or gatekeeper	Grasses	Bramble and hedges
	Meadow brown	Grasses	Meadows
	Small heath	Grasses	Grassland and heath
	Large heath (*)	Cotton Grasses	Moorland
	Ringlet	Grasses	Woodland rides
Fritillaries	Small pearl-bordered fritillary	Violets	Open woodland
	Pearl-bordered fritillary	Violets	Open woodland
	Queen of Spain fritillary (M)	–	Meadows and scrub
	Dark green fritillary	Violets, persicaria	Heath, moor and wood
	High brown fritillary	Violets	Woodland clearings
	Silver-washed fritillary (*)	Violets	Woodland clearings
	Marsh fritillary (*)	Devil's bit scabious	Wetlands
	Glanville fritillary (**)	Plantain, hawkweed, knapweed	Meadows
	Heath fritillary (**P)	Cow-wheat, plantain	Meadows
Nymphalids	Red admiral (mostly M)	Nettle, thistle	Most places
	Painted lady (M)	Nettle, thistle	Most places
	Small tortoiseshell	Nettle	Most places
	Large tortoiseshell (**)	Elm	Light woodland
	Peacock	Nettle	Most places
	Comma	Nettle, willow, hop, elm	Woodland edge
	Purple emperor (**)	Willow esp *Salix caprea*	Woodland
	White admiral (*)	Honeysuckle	Woodland
	Duke of Burgundy fritillary (**)	Cowslip, primrose	Woodland clearings
Blues	Long-tailed blue (M)	–	Flowery banks
	Little blue (*)	Birds-foot trefoil, vetch, clove	Grassy banks
	Silver-studded blue (*)	Birds-foot trefoil, gorse etc	Heaths, coasts
	Brown argus (*)	Rock rose, stork's bill	Calcareous heath
	Northern brown argus (*)	Rock rose	Sheltered moorland
	Common blue	Birds-foot trefoil, vetches, clover	Meadows
	Chalkhill blue (*)	Horseshoe vetch	Calcareous heath
	Adonis blue (**)	Horseshoe vetch	Calcareous meadows
	Large blue (**P)	Wild thyme	Downs
	Holly blue	Ivy, holly, buckthorn	Light woodland
Coppers	Small copper	Sheep sorrel, dock	Heath
	Large copper (**)	Water docks	Fen
Hairstreaks	Green hairstreak (*)	Gorse, broom, ling	Heath
	Brown hairstreak (*)	Sloe, plum	Light woodland, scrub
	Purple hairstreak (*)	Oak	Woodland
	White-letter hairstreak (*)	Elm	Woods or hedges
	Black hairstreak (M)	Sloe, plum etc	Hedge, scrub, wood
Swallowtails	Swallow-tail (**P)	Fennel, wild carrot	Fen
Whites	Large white	Crucifers esp brassica species	Most places
	Small white	Crucifers esp brassica species	Most places
	Green-veined white	Crucifers	Marsh, woodland
	Bath white (M)	–	Meadows
	Orange-tip	Hedge garlic, lady's smock etc	Meadows and clearings
Yellows	Clouded yellow (M)	Vetches	Heath
	Brimstone	Buckthorns	Light woodland
	Wood white (**)	Legumes incl trefoil, tuberous pea	Woodland

list continued opposite

Skippers	Dingy skipper	Trefoil, sea-holly	Meadows
	Grizzled skipper	Cinquefoils, mallow, agrimony	Bogs, meadows
	Chequered skipper (**P)	Grasses esp brome	Light woodland
	Small skipper	Grasses	Meadows, woodland rides
	Essex skipper (**)	Grasses	
	Lulworth skipper (**)	Brome grass	Damp meadows
	Silver-spotted skipper (**)	Grasses esp tussock-grass	Downs
	Large skipper	Grasses	Meadows, woodland rides

(A few species which are rare migrants only have not been listed)

L. Species adapted to conifer woods

It is worth noting that several species have adapted to the habitat produced by secondary woodland and a normal forest rotation of conifers. One of the best examples is the nightjar. This unusual bird is known to be adapted to heathland on which birch has begun to colonise sparsely, and we have already seen that heathland is a habitat which has been fast disappearing in recent years. Although the nightjar is in decline, it is not being displaced altogether from heathlands which have been afforested, provided there are always parts of the plantation in the early pre-thicket stage. These areas mimic heathland to the nightjar's satisfaction, and have indeed become a major stronghold for the species in several parts of Britain. One of the conservation advantages of forestry plantations, which rangers should seek to preserve, where appropriate, is that they are often relatively undisturbed. This is a great advantage to the ground-nesting nightjar and many other birds and animals, eg partridge and deer.

Species which have similarly adapted to forestry plantations, and in some cases flourished there, include several of the warblers, such as the grasshopper warbler in late pre-thickets; many birds of prey, which have found a sanctuary from gamekeepers and falconers, such as sparrowhawks and goshawks; also predatory mammals such as pine martens, polecats and wild cats; most deer species, which would otherwise have declined for want of sufficiently large areas of shelter and seclusion; and a few curious examples, such as stonechats, which have been observed to breed in the windrows of stumps of a post-windthrow plantation.

By contrast, there are those species which were adapted to conifer woodland in the first place. Not surprisingly, many of these, such as the long-eared owl, crossbill, coal tit, siskin, redpoll and goldcrest, have strengthened their populations in the new conifer woods.

The red squirrel presents a rather special case. This native squirrel appears to be less well adapted to the predominantly deciduous and open habitat of Britain than its introduced North American relative, the grey squirrel. The red squirrel must now contend not only with the effect of the disease to which it is periodically prone in Great Britain, but also this increased competition, and in the new equation it has already lost a great deal of ground. It has been predicted that the red squirrel will ultimately be restricted to pure conifer woods (preferably Scots pine, but also larch, spruce and other pines) of sufficient size to deter colonisation by juvenile greys. This provides the unusual case where not planting any hardwood belts appears to be the correct conservation measure to protect the red squirrel, where it survives, as these hardwood belts will serve as avenues of introduction to the grey squirrel.

Nightjar

Wildlife map key

HABITAT NOTES

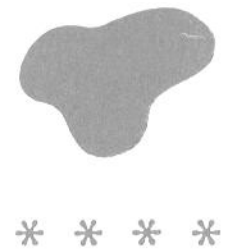	*Open or semi-open deer glade area*
	Hardwoods, especially mature wooded deer glade
	Scrub area of value to wildlife
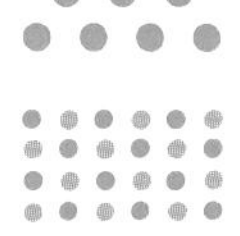	*Undergrowth of value to wildlife*
	Green ride or linear deer glade
	*Hedge of value to wildlife*
	*Crab apples, or other fruiting trees*
	*Site of named species, or of interesting flora*
	*Mature conifers left for wildlife reasons, e.g. Caledonian pine, deer glade, batbox site*

CONSERVATION

PRIMARY FLORA	*Area of primary woodland flora*
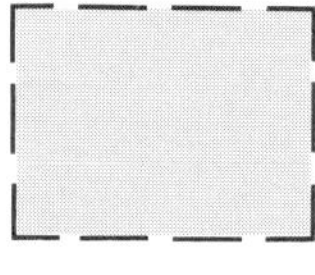	*Conservation area with boundary shown*
S.S.S.I.	*Site of Special Scientific Interest*
	*Arrow highlights small conservation site with explanation*
	*Reference to file number in Conservation File*

WILDLIFE – GENERAL

✱B ✱F ✱W ✱A ✱O ✱P — *Mammal earths (badger, fox, warren, artificial, otter, pine-marten, etc.)*

Ⓗ Ⓞ Ⓒ Ⓡ — *Bird roosts or breeding nests (heron, owl, corvids, raptors, etc.)*

Blackgame lek

PRIMARY WOODLAND FLORA
WOOD ANTS
BREEDING FROGS & NEWTS → *Miscellaneous wildlife information with pointer*

Target note (refers to further information on side of map or in Conservation File)

DEER

Major rutting stand

Bucks in summer (with direction of movement indicated)

Stags in summer

Major run from shelter to feeding grounds

High seat

Salt lick, feeding place

W — *Wallow*

Playring, play area

Deer casualty area (especially roads)

Deer sanctuary

××××××××× — *Deer fence*

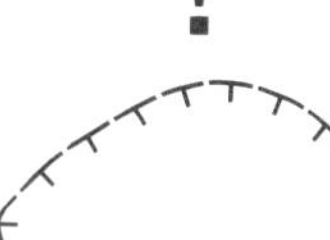

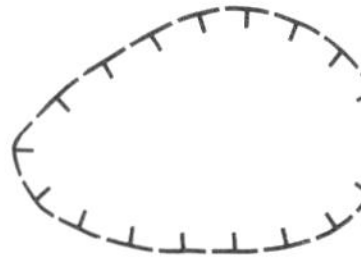

Site of recurrent deer damage

FALLOW DEER
and
SIKA DEER

STRAY RED
STAGS ONLY

Description of deer species present

RECREATION

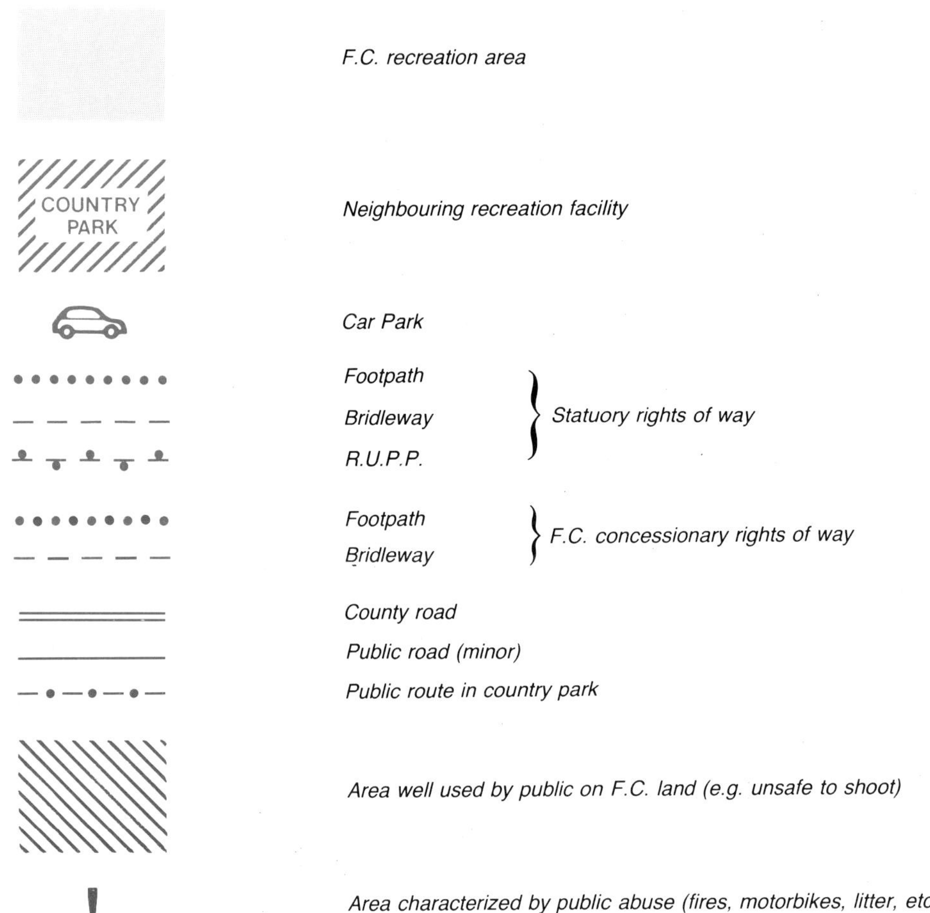

SPORTING

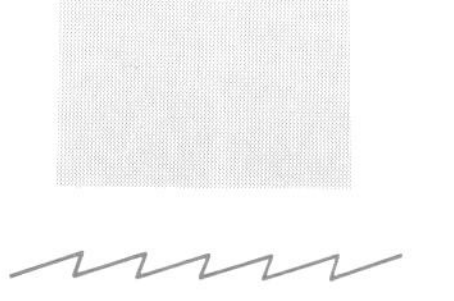

Background shading – area shot by F.C. tenant or reserved shooting

Boundary between different shoots

Identifies F.C. tenancy (number refers to lease reference) or retained shoot

KEEPER JOHN BETTS INVERGORDON 367

Name and telephone number of keeper

Fish management area, with information

LEASE 104

Duck flighting, with information

CHEMICALS

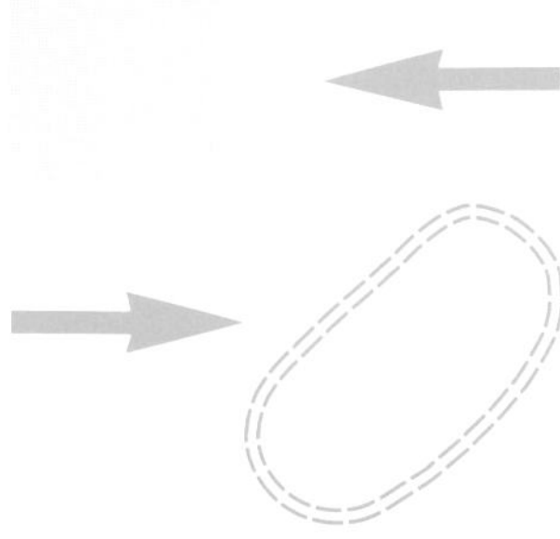

Ban on chemical spraying in operation

Recorded incidents of poison misuse

CROP DAMAGE AND NEIGHBOURS

RABBITS
(from railway embankment)

Miscellaneous information on recurrent damage sites

(N.B. More transitional or sporadic damage recorded on separate crop protection plan.)

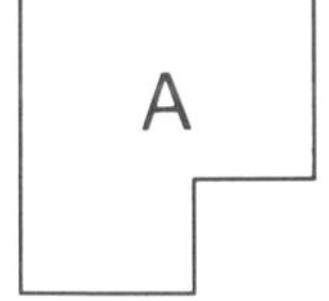

Agricultural land inside forest

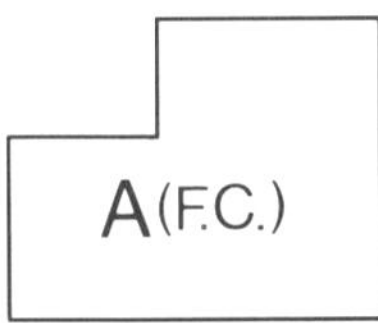

F.C. agricultural land

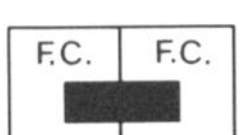

F.C. house and garden

Keepers House

Concurrent F.C. deer rights with S. Bowring

Farmer G. FITZHERBERT MANSFIELD 71642

Other general information on nearby property

WATER

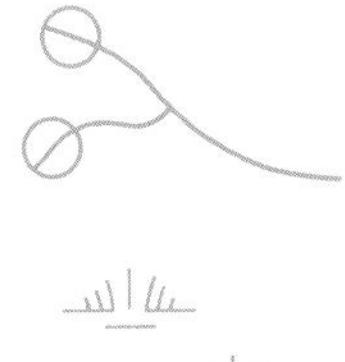

Stream with springs

Wetland, marsh, bog

Small water surface and description

Arrow highlights small water surface or dewpond

Ephemeral water feature, dewpond

FOREST ROADS, GEOLOGICAL FEATURES

Forest road

Land Rover access

Path

Bridge

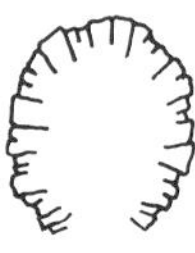

Quarry

Dam

HISTORICAL

Marker or boundary stone

Arrow highlights marker stone or other small historical feature

Earthwork

Old parish boundary, woodland edge or other linear conservation feature of interest

M. Wildlife map and conservation plan

Many rangers have a natural aversion to anything which involves putting pen to paper, or drawing on a map! It is worth being clear about the advantages to both wildlife and forest staff of a wildlife map and conservation plan. Without such a plan, the management or even the existence of a conservation area (whether for rare plants, badgers, fish or reptiles) depends largely on a spoken agreement involving the present forester (or forest manager) and the ranger, whereas a plan lays down the areas agreed for wildlife. Even in the case of SSSIs (Site of Special Scientific Interest – see later in this chapter) there can be considerable room for confusion (can the forester spray? or plant conifers?) unless there is a conservation plan in the office which the forester knows he can consult, rather than some half heard-of agreement with the national countryside agency. A wildlife map is also of considerable use to the forest manager when planning the zoning of land-use in his forest so as to avoid conflicts between wildlife, shooting or fishing, and public recreation. Another point is that a record of fixed wildlife features could be of great value in a wildlife emergency such as, in the case of a rabies outbreak, the need to know where fox-earths and badger setts are. Finally a plan is of value to the Forestry Commission when discussing our conservation and wildlife considerations with outside bodies and societies.

The following suggestions for a standardised wildlife map and conservation plan have been tried in practice for several years, and are adaptable to the needs of different forests. The wildlife and the conservation plan are separate, but equally important, parts.

The wildlife map should be of as large a scale as possible (preferably 1:10000 scale, especially if available in a composite form for the forest), and it should be in permanent use, preferably pinned up on the wall of the ranger's office. On it the ranger can mark just about everything connected with wildlife that concerns him and the forester: all the major fox-earths and badger setts (this map will only be shown to selected members of the public, nonetheless it is important to use symbols for sensitive pieces of information such as badger setts or nesting sites of birds of prey); conservation areas for rare plants; main deer runs, rutting stands and salt licks; areas which should not be sprayed with herbicide; streams, pools and belts of natural vegetation; shooting tenancies and keepers' addresses.

At first this seems rather a mixture of information to put all on one map, but the key (given on the previous 5 pages) is designed so that each colour represents a different subject. Consequently it is easy to focus your eyes on, for example, any orange-coloured marks when looking for deer information, or light blue when looking for water features, or purple when looking for recreation information. No doubt there will be several features in different forests not yet covered by the key, but using this system as a basis, it is easy to devise new symbols in the appropriate colour. (The ranger will find that ordinary felt-tips are available in these colours, and a full set should be kept by the map at all times. Background shadings are made with crayons, eg Rowney Victoria). Such general wildlife information will be scattered over the ranger's whole area, but there will also be small areas of the forest on which wildlife management or conservation is given some form of priority, and this is where the conservation plan comes in. Conservation areas are marked on the wildlife map, but you will need to refer to a file in the conservation plan for details. The most important thing in this file will be a management plan written by the forest district manager giving precise details about how the conservation area will be managed. Other pieces of information such as species lists or reports by outside bodies may be kept in the same file.

In many cases these conservation areas will be Sites of Special Scientific Interest (SSSIs), which is the title given to nationally-recognised conservation areas determined by the national countryside agency. In this case the conservation plan will have been formulated by the forest district manager as usual, but also agreed to by the national countryside agency, and as such it is a binding agreement under the terms of the 1981 Wildlife and Countryside Act. It is also worth including the site description of the SSSI in the file. When the ranger begins compiling the conservation file, he will obviously wish to start with the SSSIs in his area, and also consider other national designations, eg Areas of Outstanding Natural Beauty (AONBs) or national park boundaries.

In other instances, however, there will be areas which, though not nationally designated, are still managed by the Forestry Commission with special consideration for conservation (eg a wildlife pool and surroundings, a reptile conservation area) and it is important to have management plans for the future of these conservation areas. It may equally well be worth keeping the mowing plan for the forest in a separate file, if rides and verges and clearings are mowed or swiped for wildlife. This is best encapsulated in two facing pieces of clear plastic book-covering stuck together round the margin, so that it may be used year after year by the tractor driver.

Once the wildlife map and conservation plan have been put into practice, the ranger may consider other maps which could be useful to him. One such is a map hanging in the ranger's or forester's office on which foresters may mark any areas on which serious crop damage is occurring (using a different colour for deer, rabbits, insects, squirrels etc). and also all vulnerable areas, ie young plantations, and crops vulnerable to squirrel attack which can usually be supplied by computer print-out. This helps to direct ranger effort towards priority areas. Another useful map is a wildlife map for display to the general public. This is taken from the ranger's wildlife map, but with the most sensitive pieces of information left out, and particular emphasis placed on zoning of the forest into areas used for conservation, recreation and sporting, each of which may be emphasised by the appropriate colour of background shading.

It was suggested in Section 1 that one of the great advantages of wildlife conservation in forestry is that truly long-term schemes may be carried out, which are the most valuable ones for wildlife. It should quickly be obvious that a simple, practical system of wildlife records and plans will provide continuity and a guarantee into the future for wildlife.

N. Conservation planning – NW(E) Technical Instruction

1. Introduction

Much good work has already been done by district, forest and ranger staff to identify and record the nature conservation resource. This instruction is intended to consolidate exisiting data and systems.

2. Objectives

2.1 To select sites of conservation interest and identify their needs so as to provide local managers with guidance on how best to integrate conservation with other aspects of forest management.

2.2 To ensure continuity of management so that sites are not overlooked with the passage of time or with changes in staff.

3. General

The primary objective of forest management is economic timber production but there are many secondary objectives of which conservation and recreation are pre-eminent. There are some aspects of these 2 general activities which are incompatible. It will be necessary to design recreational facilities to minimise the impact on the conservation interests, and in some cases the forest will be zoned with the presumptions for and against these activites. There is also a possible conflict between forest protection and the conservation of some animals, particularly deer. The policy laid down gives protection priority but in general terms encourages conservation objectives to minimise damage to forest crops.

4. Selection of conservation sites

4.1 Conservation sites are designated by 2 statutory authorities, the national countryside agency who define the designated Sites of Special Scientific Interest (SSSIs) which may be for any aspect of wildlife or geology; and the Historic Building and Monuments Commission, who define and schedule ancient monuments. The Countryside Commission defines Areas of Outstanding Natural Beauty, but the interests of this body and that of the National Parks lies outside the scope of this instruction.

4.2 Sites may also be defined locally by Forestry Commission staff to cover any aspect of natural history, geology, archaeology or design to improve the aesthetic appearance of the forest as a whole or site within the forest. Such sites where they are for a specific purpose, may overlap SSSIs which have a general designation.

4.3 The basic criteria for the designation of a site of local conservation interest will be that "the conservation objectives are at least as or more important than other management objectives (usually economic timber production)", eg badger sett, blackcock lek, area of herb paris. The minimum area for such sites will be 0.5 hectares. Where small sites are of special value, eg a patch of military orchids, their area will be made up to 0.5 hectares by a buffer zone. These criteria have been found to work in practice and to give a clear definition of the important sites which may require special management measures.

4.4 Individual sites of under 0.5 hectares and linear features of interest, eg old hedgerows within plantations, and agricultural land, are not to be included unless of special interest. They will be catered for by management following the wildlife conservation measures given in the Forestry Commission booklet No 29 'Wildlife Conservation in Woodlands'.

5. Recording

5.1 Brief data will be recorded on the format given in Appendix I. All conservation sites will be numbered consecutively but separate schedules should be kept for designated SSSIs, ancient monuments and forest designated conservation areas. The data on these schedules is intended to indicate the interest and to be the means of entry into more detailed records.

5.2 There will be many occasions when there are few if any details for sites, but for others there could be a wealth of detail provided by either amateur or professional bodies. If details are available then these should either be kept at the forest office or sufficient information should be available to call upon the data when required, ie names, addresses, dates of study, etc. It is important that we build up our knowledge of what studies have been and are being done in forests, but the precise details of how this information is kept at the forest is left to local forest district manager to decide. It is, therefore, important to include in a permission for a survey/study that the Forestry Commission has free access to the data whenever necessary.

6. Liaison with outside bodies

6.1 The national liaison arrangements with the national countryside agency have been agreed and the same spirit of co-operation will be followed with the voluntary bodies, eg Nature Conservation Trusts, Royal Society for the Protection of Birds. In particular forest district managers should make a point of contacting the countryside regional officers in their district who will always be willing to assist and advise.

6.2 Care must be exercised by forest district managers when giving permission to study particular conservation subjects to limit the number of individuals so as to ensure that no damage occurs, particularly to the more sensitive sites/species. Advice may be sought from the countryside regional officers upon the bona fides of unknown naturalists who apply for permission to study in our forests.

6.3 Whilst we make every effort to obtain as much information as possible, it must be clearly understood that the Forestry Commission will manage its woodlands taking account of the conservation interest. There will be rare cases where an outside body undertakes the management of small clearly defined areas of Forestry Commission land; such cases will be agreed by the conservator upon the recommendation of the forest district manager.

7. Implementation

7.1 It is the responsibility of the district forester (FM) to compile the draft forest conservation plan.

7.2 At its simplest the forest conservation plan will consist of:

(i) An introductory statement of policies, eg ride cutting, maintenance of ponds, treatment of broadleaves on clear felling sites, sitting and maintenance of deer glades

(ii) A stock map marked with all the conservation sites, each site being shown by a form of shading. Alongside each area will be the site number in a circle.

(iii) The brief details given on the schedule (see Appendices I and II). It is possible that these data may be included on the computer data base at some future date, and in anticipation of this event the presence of all conservation sites should be listed on the compartment description, form WPO.

7.3 Managers will use their wildlife staff, who will be overseen by the head rangers, and any other expert to identify and describe conservation sites.

7.4 Forest district managers will discuss the draft plan with the district forester (FM) and head ranger, he will agree the locally defined sites (calling for advice from the Conservancy Wildlife Adviser if necessary) and the proposed management prescriptions and formally approve the plan. Thereafter the approved provisions will be incorporated into normal programmes and budgets.

7.5 It is not anticipated that these plans will require revision on predetermined dates; they are likely to be more dynamic and will be added to as and when extra resources or details are identified. The district forester (FM) will be responsible for ensuring that as much information as possible is collected by encouraging Naturalist Trusts and other such organisations and bona fide individuals to study particular aspects of natural history in the forest. This will be an ongoing duty which is best taken slowly and progressively. It will be the responsibility of forest district managers to ensure that the forest conservation plan is progressed and kept properly up to date.

Dated 24 November 1981.

Appendix I

Schedule of local */countryside agency*/Ancient Monuments* Conservation Sites

Subject ....

Site no	Cpt no	Area (Ha)	Description	Remarks	Proposed management	Date due and done/remarks

*Delete as appropriate

Appendix II
Notes on the completion of the schedule of conservation sites

1. Separate schedules will be kept of the sites designated by the national countryside agency, HB & MC and by the Forestry Commission. Some of the sites designated by the Forestry Commission may, in due course, be included in the other lists.
2. The schedules may be kept by subject, but in any event locally designated sites of archaelogical interest should be kept separately from those of wildlife interest.
3. In the schedule of SSSIs the 6-figure National Grid reference should be included with, but under the compartment number, and the grade of the site included under the Remarks column.
4. The 6-figure National Grid reference should be included for scheduled ancient monuments. If the monument has a name it should begin the 'Description'. Under the 'Remarks' column note any other relevant information.
5. The column headed 'Description' is intended for a brief description only of the reasons for the designation and of the existing land use, eg crop. Full descriptions, eg species lists, are better filed separately.

Section 3
Crop protection

A. The first steps:
   Prevention, location and identification of damage

B. Damage assessment techniques

C. Rabbits
   i. History and habits
   ii. Planning the control programme
   iii. Fenced plantations
   iv. Unfenced plantations
   v. Damage complaints from neighbours

D. Hares

E. Squirrels
   i. History and habits
   ii. Planning the control programme
   iii. Grey squirrel control
   iv. Red squirrel control
   v. Squirrels and the law
   vi. Use of Warfarin

F. Voles

G. Insects and fungi

H. Domestic stock

I. Birds

J. Species not harmful to forestry: foxes, mink etc

A. The first steps:
Prevention, location and identification of damage

The job of crop protection does not begin with pest control, but with prevention of damage. Even before any trees are planted, the ranger should study the area and consider the following questions: What species are present which may do damage, and in what numbers? What is the potential for colonisation or increase by these species? How could the forest be planned to minimize damage? To what extent should damage considerations influence the species of trees to be planted, and the design of compartments? Is fencing against rabbits, hares, deer or domestic animals necessary and economic, or not?

In short, crop protection must be seen as part of a wider process of planning of the forest to avoid as many problems as may be foreseen from experience, and to provide as varied an environment as possible. This is why protection is inseparable from the other aims of forestry, which are production, recreation and conservation. It is also why crop protection is not a matter of waiting for damage to occur before dealing with it. The first essential steps of crop protection are prediction and prevention of damage as far as possible within the overall forest plan.

The other important aspect of prevention is that unforeseen damage, when it does occur, needs to be located in its earliest possible stage. This requires the ranger to be patrolling his area on foot, and acting as the eyes and ears of the Forestry Commission at all times. The next step is accurate damage identification before an assessment is made of the severity of damage and action taken.

In other words, the ranger who waits to be told of damage, and controls only the species he is told to control by his forester, is fulfilling very few of the important parts of his job.

The following pages provide a field guide to identifying the forms of damage encountered on and near the forest.

(1) Stripping by deer

Species: Red, sika and fallow. Very rarely roe.

Time of year: Usually most severe January – March and during snow. May carry on for longer, especially in Scotland.

Description: Stripping occurs when deer shave off tree-bark with their lower teeth for food. The broad parallel teeth-marks are often clearly visible, running more or less vertically*. The worst stripping arises when large numbers of deer, usually seeking shelter from severe weather, are concentrated into areas of woodland they do not normally inhabit.

Stripping by red deer on rowan showing teeth-marks

Thicket-stage plantations are often worst attacked, but damage may occur on any tree from around seven years onwards. Highly vulnerable species are Norway spruce, lodgepole pine (especially thicket stage) and most hardwoods (especially young elm). Douglas and silver firs, Lawson cypress, hemlock and young Sitka spruce, Scots pine and larch may also be damaged. Brashing of any tree species increases vulnerability. *(Width of toothmark – red 9.5 mm; fallow/sika 6.4 mm. Typical height from ground – red < 1.7 m, fallow/sika < 1.1 m, roe 0.4 m < 0.6 m).

Red deer stripping on lodgepole pine

Comment: Stripping is the worst form of damage which red and sika can inflict, and prevention is a main baseline for control of these species, especially in the north. See red deer management strategy, Section 4 E.

Elm saplings stripped by fallow deer

(2) Browsing by deer (and sheep)

Species: All deer (also sheep, see Section 3H below)

Time of year: Peak of damage January – May, while other food is scarce and buds and growing shoots most tender. Can occur at all times of year.

Description: Browsing is the nibbling of the buds and shoots of newly-established trees, in particular, for food. Trees browsed by deer often develop multi-leaders, or in severe cases come to resemble clipped miniature bushes. Vulnerability to browsing is mainly relative to the amount of other browse available, but species preferred for stripping are also preferred for browsing, and browsing is also more likely to occur soon after planting and in certain sites, eg trees planted in clearing to which deer have become accustomed to grazing, slopes which remain clear of snow in winter, young plantations surrounded by a thicket-stage crop where deer can shelter. It is essential to be able to distinguish deer browse from sheep, rabbit and hare browsing damage (see illustrations at (5) page 60).

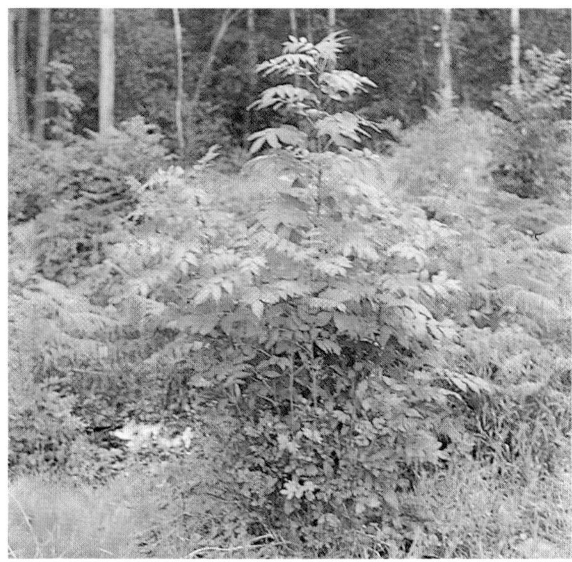
Muntjac browsing on ash coppice

Multi-leaders on Sitka spruce resulting from sheep browsing

Comment: Browsing is not as obvious as stripping or fraying, but builds up during the early years of a plantation, and becomes a severe form of damage when it prevents an adequate percentage of leading shoots growing beyond the reach of deer (muntjac 1 m – red 2 m). In some areas browsing imposes a 2-4 year delay on the time taken by Sitka spruce to grow beyond reach, greater delays could have serious economic consequences. Browsing of side shoots is not a significant form of damage.

Prevention is achieved by adequate culling policy and forest design (see 'Deer management'). Overall chemical weeding increases browsing by reducing other available browse. Fencing may be necessary in some situations (eg a block of hardwoods in an otherwise conifer wood), but should be seen as a last resort.

A Scots pine browsed by fallow deer – multi-leaders have resulted

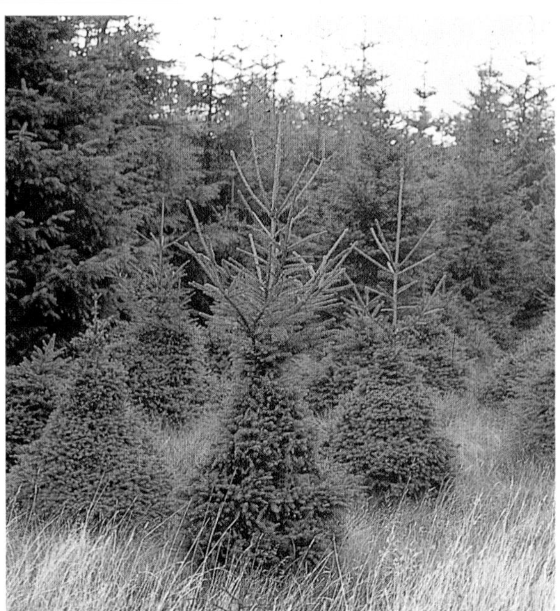

Severe browsing on Norway spruce by roe deer

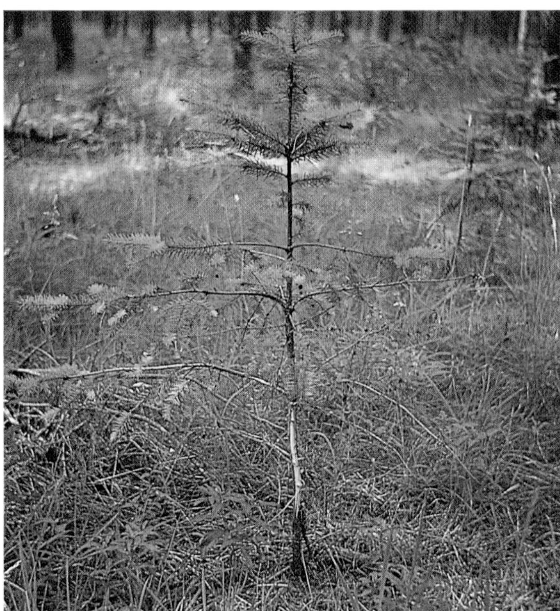

Roe deer fraying

(3) Fraying

Species: All deer (male)

Time of year: Roe – mainly March to August. Other species – mainly August to November with a lesser outbreak in Spring.

Description: Fraying is caused by male deer rubbing their antlers (and facial scent glands) against tree stems and foliage. This is mostly a form of sexual aggression or territory-marking which occurs during the build-up to the rut. Fraying is recognised, on close examination, by the presence of hairs in and around the damage, also by accompanying broken and twisted side-branches and associated scrapes on the ground. Fraying is frequently found near to places where deer come into the open, also on aromatic trees or trees with a different scent from the main crop, and this fortunately results in scrub trees (eg willow, birch, rowan) outside the commercial crop being selected if present. The species of deer responsible can usually be distinguished as follows:

Muntjac – up to 400 mm off ground, frequently on stem only without damage to side branches, frequently in open woodland rather than woodland edges, tooth-marks often present, mostly on very thin stems (25 mm) but some bole-scoring on thick stems, muntjac fraying occurs August – May.

Roe – mostly up to 750 mm from ground, undersides of branches on stem damaged.

Fallow – thicker stems (75 mm) up to 1.2 m, thrashed stems to 2 m.

Sika – similar height to fallow; in some populations, areas of severe bole-scoring recorded on mature trunks up to 300 mm diameter, especially spruce.

Red – thick stems with severe damage to branches and tops, no scrapes associated.

Comment: Although often the most conspicuous form of deer damage fraying is usually the least serious. Roe deer fraying, which starts when the trees are more tender, continues for several months and is widely spread through the wood because of the territorial nature of roe, is more serious than fraying by other species. Control of juvenile bucks, which may cause more damage than territory-markers, is of importance. A strip of scrub left on the plantation edge provides alternative fraying-stocks.

(4) Deer damage in fields and gardens

Species: All deer.

Time of year and description: In winter, root crops such as swedes can be severely damaged, especially if farmed close to the forest edge. Large groups of deer will also gather on winter cereals and grass, but most farmers accept that deer rarely cause significant damage to these crops before the onset of the growing season, in spring, when it is often useful to concentrate on fields for culling. By May/June crops are tall enough for deer to lie in unseen, but it is too late to consider culling does and hinds, so it is fortunate that they are about to split up for fawning, when the amount of damage that they cause is greatly reduced. On the other hand bucks and stags of the herding species (red, sika and fallow) are joining in large groups, often further away from the main woods than at any other time, and it is sometimes necessary to respond to complaints about their marauding damage. Succulent crops such as peas and soft fruits are especially vulnerable. In late summer potatoes may be dug by deer, especially in dry conditions, and sugar beet may be damaged.

Muntjac fraying on aspen

Fallow deer fraying

Sika bole-scoring

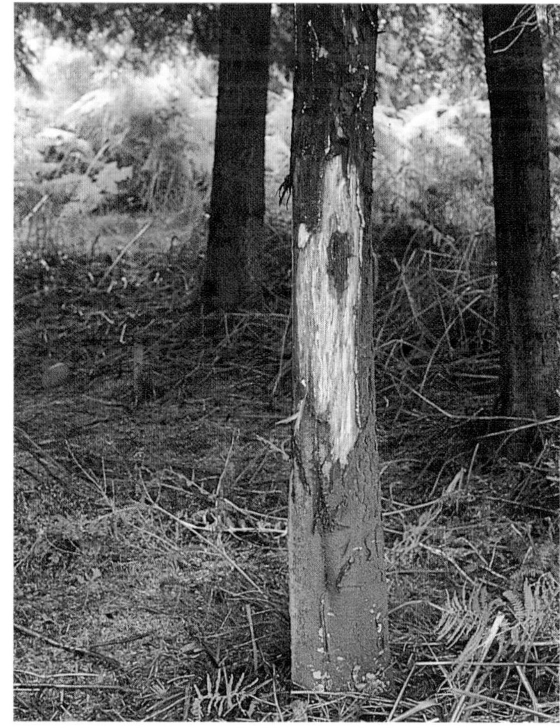

Red deer fraying on large bole

Co-operation in management plans with farmers is the key to dealing with deer damage on fields, especially by assessing and discussing the seriousness of damage, seeking permission to cull on fields, entering into carcass-sharing agreements, and advising on vulnerable crops which are best kept furthest from the forest edge. The ranger should leave his telephone number with all farmers on whose land deer from his forest may travel, and if this system of co-operation is implemented, farm damage by deer is rarely severe.

Gardens and market gardens in or adjacent to the forest present special problems, to which the only successful long-term solution is fencing, though this advice is rarely heeded.

(5) Browsing (rabbits and hares)

Species: Rabbit, brown hare, mountain hare.

Time of year: Usually most severe in winter and early spring, especially during snow conditions which may also bring taller trees within reach.

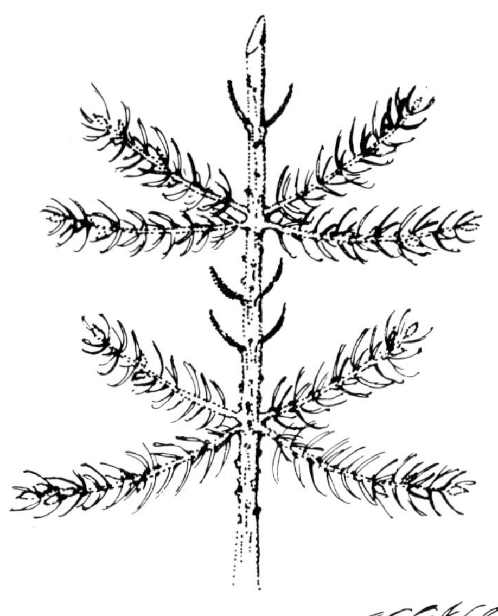

Rabbit or hare browse
Clean, often diagonal cut
Shoot often left lying

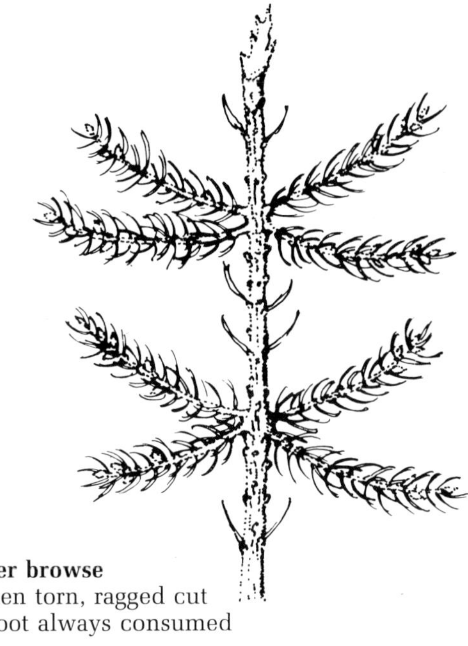

Deer browse
Often torn, ragged cut
Shoot always consumed

Description: Browsing by rabbits and hares is distinguished from deer-browsing by the following points (a) the cut is clean (and usually oblique) because rabbits and hares have lower and upper incisors (front cutting teeth), whereas deer (and indeed sheep) have to sheer a woody shoot between lower incisors and the hard pad in upper jaw, leaving a torn edge. (b) Some or all of the browsed shoots frequently not consumed and found lying on the ground, especially in the case of hares in winter. (c) Except after snow, which brings taller trees within reach, at a lower level, usually from ground level to 150 mm. To distinguish between hare and rabbit browsing the above points may be considered, also any associated sign, eg droppings, rabbit scrapes. Rabbits tend to browse progressively from cover, whereas hares often browse down a line of trees.

Comment: Browsing is invariably the most severe form of damage by rabbits and hares within the forest. For prevention, see rabbit control on pages 66-68.

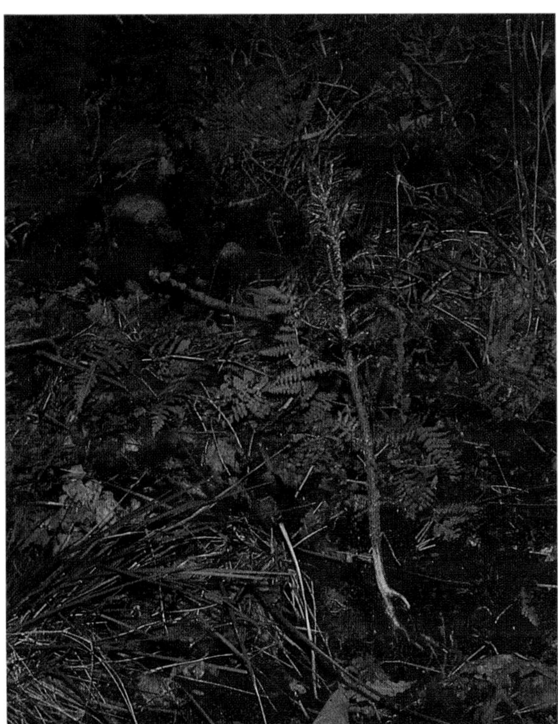

Rabbit damage to Norway spruce

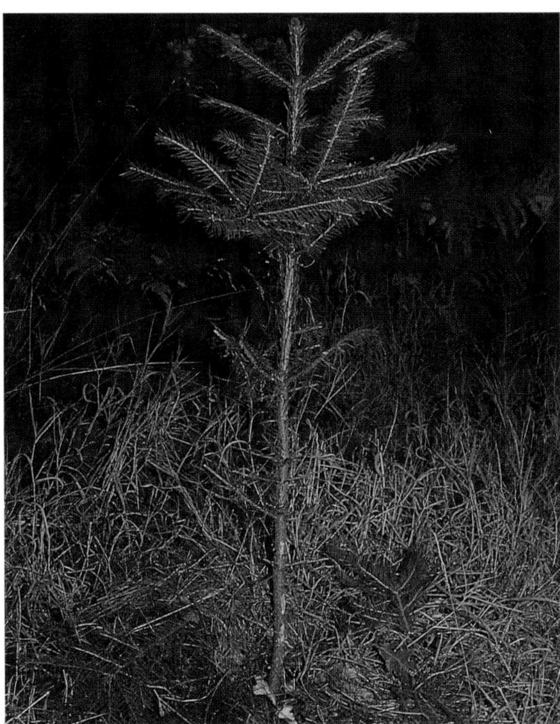

Hare damage to Norway spruce

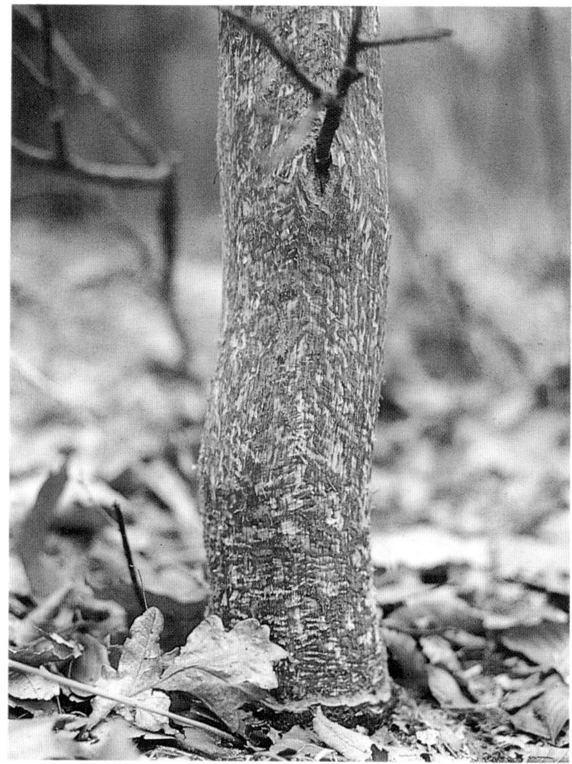

Close-up of rabbit stripping on an oak sapling

(6) Bark stripping (rabbits and hares)
Species: Rabbit, brown hare, mountain hare
Time of year: Winter and early spring, especially during snow cover when alternative food is scarce.
Description: The size and position of the bite on shrubs, hedges and small stems usually allows this damage to be readily distinguished from deer stripping, ie usually well below 600 mm off ground (except after deep snow), often on stems inaccessible to deer (eg in hedge), teeth marks often diagonally on stem, width of tooth mark less than 3.2 mm. Because upper incisors of rabbits and hares are deeply furrowed, close inspection of tooth marks reveals the appearance of four narrow furrows. Smooth-barked trees preferred. See also bark-gnawing by voles.

Occasionally rabbits and hares will attack the boles of large smooth-barked trees (eg beech), leaving an appearance of damage similar to squirrel basal damage, but usually far too early in the year for squirrel damage.
Comment: Rarely a serious or widespread form of damage.

(7) Rabbit and hare damage in fields
Species: Rabbit, brown hare, mountain hare
Time of year: All year round, but usually most harmful in winter, and especially spring.
Description: Grazing damage by rabbits in fields adjacent to the shelter of woods and hedges advances in a clear line away from this shelter (whereas deer grazing tends to be more evenly scattered across a field, less tightly-cropped, and as a consequence of these two factors less harmful). It should be remembered that there are several other possible causes for agricultural crop failure (eg game-bird scratching, slugs, flooding, faulty drilling, insect pests, disease, even squirrel scratching) so that, as always, it is essential to begin by identifying the exact type of damage. Rabbit scrapes and droppings are invariably present, and leaves of crop clearly cut by grazing.

Rabbit damage to beech in late winter — (not squirrel damage!)

Rabbit damage to wheat – progressing in a clear line from cover

Because hares are rarely found in dense populations, grazing by hares is usually less severe, and (like deer) more evenly scattered across a field.

Rabbits and hares, in particular, attack winter root crops in a similar way to deer by gnawing the roots. The size of tooth-mark is an easy distinguishing mark from deer.

Comment: Can be a major problem for the ranger, see Sections 3 C v and 3 D on pages 66-68 for details.

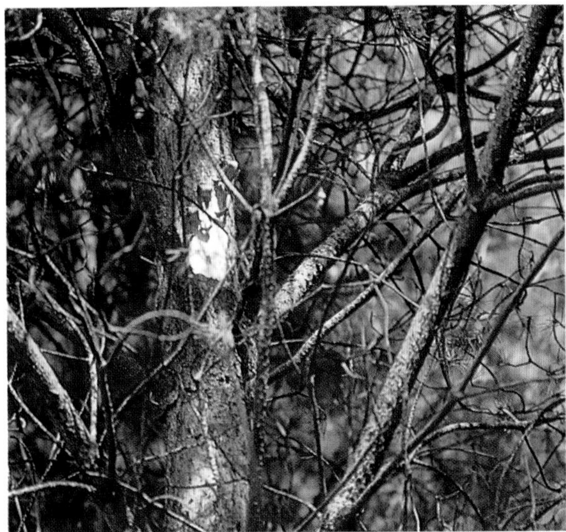

Red squirrel damage on Corsican pine – note curls of bark

Close-up of grey squirrel damage to beech – note chips of bark

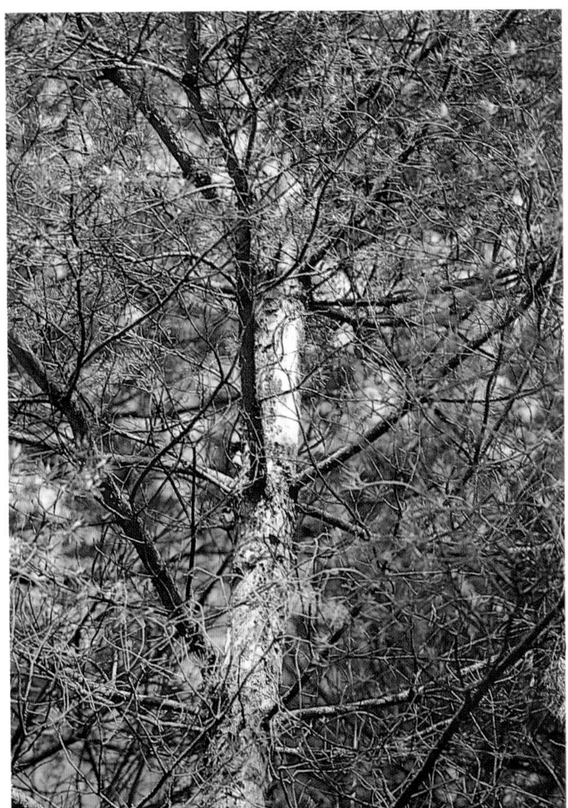

Grey squirrel damage to Scots pine

Grey squirrel damage to beech

(8) Squirrel damage

Species: Grey squirrel, red squirrel.

Time of year: March – September, principally mid May – mid July.

Description: Bark stripped off the trunk or main boughs of grown trees (10-50 years) during the summer months, most commonly (i) starting at ground level, known as 'basal damage', usually grey squirrels on hardwoods only (ii) at several points above where the main boughs of hardwoods meet the trunk, both on the main trunk or on these boughs (iii) on the main stems of conifers, usually high up in the last 10 years of growth, both grey and red squirrels. The outer bark is characteristically not consumed, but remains in coils on the tree, or in coils and chips on the ground.

Species favoured by grey squirrels are sycamore and beech, but pines, oaks, ash, larch, hemlock, birch and maples may all be severly affected, and the damage behaviour of grey squirrels varies considerably from one area to another.

The species favoured by red squirrels is

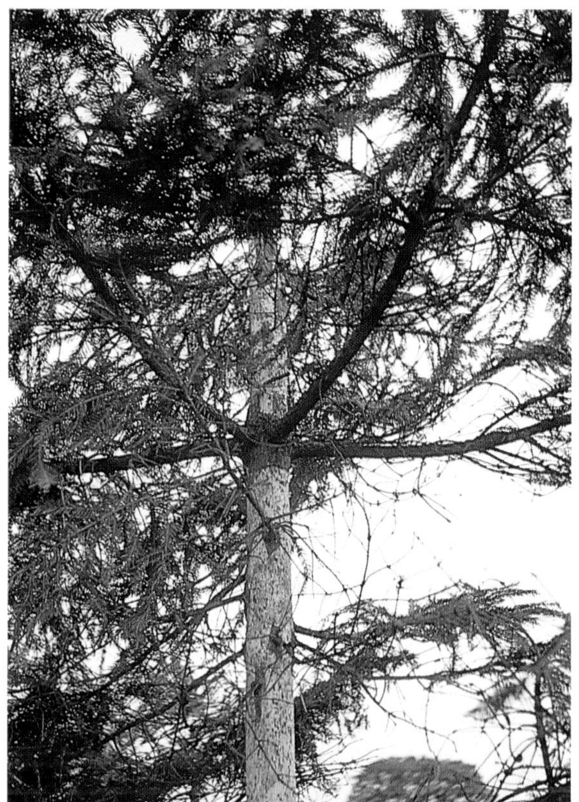

Edible dormouse damage to Douglas fir

Basal bark damage caused by field vole

Scots pine, occasionally European larch, lodgepole pine and Norway spruce, less commonly other species.

Comment: Grey squirrel damage is one of the severest and most widespread hindrances to commercial timber growing, because trees are damaged at an advanced stage, and prevention and control is not always easy. Even if trees are not usually killed, they become prone to severe windsnap after squirrel damage. Red squirrels do not so commonly build their numbers up to the point of doing serious damage.

Squirrels, especially grey squirrels, are occasionally responsible for other forms of damage of less widespread significance, eg removing the heads of cereal crops, bud damage to young trees, eating seeds in seed orchards, eating orchard fruit, gnawing electric wiring in house lofts.

(9) Basal bark gnawing (vole)

Species: Field vole. Occasionally water vole.

Time of year: Winter.

Description: When young trees in rank tussocky grassy plantations have their bark gnawed away in winter just above soil level, usually beneath the grass mat or underneath the cover of snow, this is invariably the work of field voles. The stem is typically laid completely bare over a small area, and minute teeth marks (width less than 1.3 mm) are discernable. If the surrounding grass mat is parted and searched, an elaborate system of vole runways and 'parlours' will be revealed, with vole droppings and small piles of grass stems cut into short lengths. Where rabbits and hares gnaw the bark of young trees the damage is generally higher up the trunk, always above the level of the grass mat, and usually not so concentrated in one small patch of gnawing, so that areas of bark remain between the larger bites. Insect damage (eg by pine weevil) occurs later in the year (April – August).

Similar damage is occasionally found on the stems and exposed roots of water-side trees such as ash, willow and poplar, caused by the far larger water vole. This is rarely of serious economic consequence.

Comment: The only serious damage caused by voles. See 'Vole control' Section 3 F.

(10) High barking (vole)

Species: Bank vole.

Time of year: Winter, especially during snow cover.

Description: This damage has a characteristic appearance, with lengths of bark gnawed away from the angle between stem and branch on small or young trees, which is evidently where the climbing bank vole sits when causing this. In Britain the damage is usually found on elder bushes during conditions of snow cover, but also on occasional pre-thicket trees in a young plantation, at a typical height of between 600 mm and 2 m above ground level. Odd trees planted for ornament and amenity sometimes affected.

Comment: Not a serious or common form of damage, rarely amounting to more than a few trees scattered through the plantation.

(11) Browsing damage (capercaillie and black grouse)

Species: Capercaillie and black game.

Time of year: Early spring especially, when expanding buds and young shoots of conifers are most palatable, and other food is scarce.

Description: Capercaillie – Terminal bud cluster, part of shoot and nearby needles may be removed. Scots pine preferred, but also spruces, larch, Douglas fir and other conifers, hardwoods rarely affected.

Black grouse – damage to the individual tree usually less widespread, with buds pecked out singly. Except in deep snow, only trees up to 600 mm high affected. Pine preferred, also larch, occasionally Sitka spruce, rarely Norway spruce or Douglas fir.

Comment: Damage is not significant unless these species are present in high numbers (up to 80% leader damage recorded for black game), and plantations which get away slowly are the worse affected. Additional damage may be caused by birds snapping off leaders by landing on them. Browsing damage to older trees is not a significant form of damage.

Blackgame damage on lodgepole pine – all leading buds eaten

(12) Insect and fungi damage

Lodgepole pine defoliated by pine beauty moth caterpillars

Spruce bark beetle *(Dendroctonus)* – resin tube at entrance point

Neomyzaphis defoliation on spruce amongst pine

Frost damage to Douglas fir plantation

Close-up of pine weevils and damage

Honey fungus attack on two Corsican pines

B. Damage assessment techniques

Once damage has been located and identified, the ranger with experience of crop damage in that forest can usually answer the question "Will that form of damage amount to an unacceptably severe attack over the years unless extra control is undertaken?"

This subjective judgement, based on experience, is often the easiest form of assessment but it may be misleading. It is helpful to know the percentage of trees damaged, especially where there is some doubt about the severity of the attack. The best system for making such a statistical assessment is called the 'Nearest Neighbour Method', a detailed explanation of which is given in FC Leaflet 82.

When making a statistical assessment, it is essential to decide beforehand exactly what type of damage is being assessed, and to record different types of damage on separate forms, even though the same clusters of trees may be used. For example, it is obviously sensible when doing an assessment of deer browsing damage, to record damage to leading shoots only or separately, as lateral damage is of little economic significance. You may in some cases choose to record separately, leader completely removed and trees with multiple leaders. It is also useful to differentiate between this year's and previous year's damage, where possible. Obviously you will never group together damage by different species on one form, as the significance of such results would be very slight. It is always possible to add together various results afterwards.

Whether assessment is made subjectively or statistically, it is essential that factors other than percentage and appearance are finally given their true weight. For example, we can suppose the existence of a Scots pine forest with roe deer, grey squirrels and hares present. Fraying damage by roe amounting to 5% of a young plantation will be concentrated on the rides and edges, and therefore look alarming, but the crop will pass out of the fraying phase in a few years and some damaged trees may recover fully. Unless browsing damage is severe, there is no reason to make a major alteration to the roe cull. On the other hand, a 5% girdling of 20 year old Scots pine tops may be barely visible, but the economic consequence could be enormous, control might be very difficult, and some serious thinking is required, which might lead to the conclusion that present methods of squirrel control are inadequate. A 5% browsing attack by hares on a young plantation may be considered the unusual result of a severe winter, justifying no action at all. One of the numerous factors to be considered in any form of assessment is whether the cost of control outweighs the cost of damage. Once again we are reminded that crop protection should never be approached as a single job requiring no thought.

C. Rabbits

i. History and habits

Enough has been said and written about the rabbit for it to be evident that this animal, a native of the Mediterranean introduced to Britain 800 years ago, is one of the most adaptable of all creatures. The only real requirement of the rabbit is any form of dry shelter within reasonable striking distance (rarely more than 400 metres) of grazing, while outside the breeding season they can survive on browse and bark.

Breeding takes place chiefly between January and August, though litters may exceptionally be found in any month of the year, and the widespread planting of winter cereals in recent years may have allowed earlier breeding in many areas. Does are sexually mature by about 4 months provided they have reached a breeding weight of around 1 kg. If conditions are suitable, they will then breed monthly during the breeding season, with an average of 5 kits in each litter. Young are born in dead-end tunnels inside the main burrow or in 'stops' running from the surface. The doe visits the young only once every 24 hours to suckle, and leaves them to fend for themselves at about 3½ weeks of age. Overpopulation may cause termination of pregnancy by 'resorption'. Late hard winters or cool wet springs are not favourable to rabbits.

ii. Planning the control programme

We have already said that the first step in any form of crop protection, before any trees are planted, is the assessment of potential for damage from any species. So with a new plantation or re-stocking areas after clear-fell, the ranger walks the area and the surrounds thoroughly and asks himself 3 questions:

(1) ***What number of rabbits are present?*** Look for freshly used burrows, with closely-grazed areas around them and on the edge of cover. Look for runs leading from feeding grounds to burrows or cover, with worn jumps about 200 mm – 300 mm apart in grass or bare soil. Look where these runs pass under rabbit fencing or through bushes for traces of fur caught on snags (hares almost always avoid squeezing through such narrow passes). Look for fresh droppings (usually less than 10 mm in diameter and dark. Hares also rounded, but larger, often paler, often more fibrous). These are sometimes accumulated in latrines (where hares only leave small groups), and are found next to shallow scrapes in the open as well. Also (in spring and summer) fresh urine patches may be found by these scrapes and on bare soil by the burrow. Look for tufts of hair where rabbits have been bucking, and for stops where does are breeding in the open. Look for footprints in the snow (hare prints show wider-splayed toes, and are far larger, so that they can barely be covered by a matchbox). For further information on rabbit signs see 'Damage identification' above.

(2) ***What is the potential for recolonisation by rabbits?*** Is there a constant supply of rabbits from neighbouring lands over which the Commission may have no control, such as railway cuttings (though British Rail will clear such rabbits on request) or keepered estates? Or from surrounding forest where rabbit holes have disappeared into thickets of young trees, brambles, briars or heaps of windthrow stumps, in other words any area nearby where the source of rabbits cannot be fully controlled.

(3) ***Should rabbit-fencing be used or not?*** This is the crucial question which lies at the end of the work assessment. In 1965 the Forestry Commission leaflet on rabbit control in woodland stated "Where timber growing is concerned, the rabbit is never a casual pest, with which it might be possible to come to terms on some 'live and let live' basis. No, it must be completely exterminated and its re-entry prevented . . . . The forester's first line of defence against the rabbit in this country is the netting fence". Since then the pendulum has swung away from this attitude, and foresters are reluctant to fence for reasons of cost. It is, however, the ranger's job to advise where it would be uneconomical not to fence because of the potential for serious rabbit damage. The correct solution to the question whether rabbit-fencing should be used or not is to take each new planting area on its merits. Where there are very serious problems of rabbit-control fencing is the correct and cheapest solution when measured against the cost of damage and extra ranger time.

It should by now be clear why assessment of damage before it occurs is of such great importance, as this is the only way in which planned control can be carried out. Crop protection is not working properly if the ranger is only reacting to damage after it has occurred. With rabbits, there will be 3 different protection situations on the forest, namely fenced forest crops, unfenced forest crops, and damage complaints from neighbours.

iii. Fenced plantations

Once the decision has been made to fence a new plantation or re-stock area, it is essential that the fence should be erected at least 3 months prior to planting, preferably before the winter so that rabbits may be tracked in the snow. The first task is to ensure that the fence has been properly erected, with special attention to the base of the fence, and to gates. Also that any large piles of brash or stumps or other havens for rabbits within the fence have been destroyed. The ranger then sets about the job of clearing all rabbits within the fence. This must be carried out methodically, because to leave even one or two rabbits inside at this stage defeats the object. The ranger walks the prepared ground thoroughly up and down, in strips at most 20 metres apart, with his dog, shooting any rabbits that he can with the shotgun, and marking with a stick all burrows that he finds and which the dog puts a rabbit into. Indeed, the object at this stage is to put rabbits to ground, so a ferret must not be used. The ranger then gasses all burrows (remember that whenever using rabbit gas, the

ranger is required to be accompanied by another ranger or forest worker and to carry any appropriate antidote). But this is only half a job done. It is essential to return to the same area within a fortnight and repeat the same process, looking particularly for any burrows that have been freshly opened up. From then onwards the ranger must continue to visit the area regularly, perhaps twice a week when planting begins. His first task is to inspect the fence, especially looking for where rabbits are burrowing under the fence or getting through a gate. It may be worth setting a box-trap before blocking up such a run. Remember that if snow drifts against a fence rabbits may climb over it, and rabbit damage may appear very high up the trees after the snow has melted! When inspecting the newly planted area the ranger can carry a ferret and a few nets to deal with the odd rabbit which has found its way in, or may set a few snares or traps. The plantation must be watched over by the ranger with constant vigilance until it has passed the damage stage (usually after about 8 years).

iv. Unfenced plantations

If rabbit numbers and the potential for recolonisation are low, successful control can be carried out without fencing, provided that care is taken to anticipate the development of serious rabbit problems and the need for future control, eg features such as quarries, rubble from old buildings or roads, banks of spoil and rows of windthrow stumps should not be allowed to disappear beneath thickets of young trees, bramble and briar, for they will quickly become unreachable and indestructable warrens. Also a 3 m grass ride should be left around the perimeter of all woods where plantations are left unfenced, and around the plantations themselves. If these and any other nearby rides are swiped annually, they will permit the ranger to deal with rabbits by shooting, snaring or long-netting. While the tractor is on the wood the ranger should direct it towards areas of thick bramble and cover under mature trees which may harbour rabbits and hinder gassing or ferreting operations, still the main methods of control.

v. Damage complaints from neighbours

The following points should be considered:

(a) The legal position is straightforward. When rabbits travel on to a neighbour's land and cause damage, the neighbour is entitled to ask for action to be taken to prevent this. Failing such action, the Ministry of Agriculture is empowered to order such control. On the other hand the neighbour must be made to share responsibility for control, rather than expect the Commission to do it all, if rabbits are living on the neighbour's land as well.

(b) The first step, as in the forest, is to identify and assess the damage. Crop damage in a field may be due to faulty sowing, flooding, slugs, pheasants and a host of other causes besides rabbits. If in doubt, consult with the Pest Control Officer of the Ministry of Agriculture. If rabbits are the cause, it is essential to identify where they are coming from, and who should be sharing liability for control.

(c) The usual solution lies in establishing friendly relations with the neighbour, and for all parties concerned to control rabbits on their land. Offering to provide the neighbour with fence-wire is not the correct solution (unless the Commission has a fencing liability in its land tenure), nor is offering to provide the neighbour with rabbit gas!

(d) These solutions frequently arise on Commission leasehold land where the sporting rights are retained by the landowner. This does not alter the Commission's ultimate responsibility and right to control rabbits in any way. If the keeper offers to undertake rabbit control, it is still essential that the ranger checks this is being carried out adequately. If the ranger is carrying out control, it is obviously desirable to attempt to fit in with the keeper's requirements, which are usually that the wood be left undisturbed until February/March. If this is not compatible with adequate control or other commitments, the ranger has the right and responsibility to carry out control as and when he sees fit. But obviously he will do so with the minimum of disturbance to the sporting interests.

D. Hares

Brown hares cannot achieve the same concentration of numbers as rabbits and one hare per two hectares is probably a very high stocking even on their preferred habitat, which is agricultural land, especially in plain country. Woodland and moorland are secondary habitats, used mainly for shelter. For information on hare damage, see pages 59-60.

By the same token, hares are more difficult to control than rabbits. Traditionally hares have been controlled by shooting, but this requires a large number of people to form effective driving and shooting lines, which is probably only possible (and worthwhile) with the co-operation of nearby farming neighbours. Snaring is also of value, as hares leave clear trails on grassland in particular, and usually leave a field through a clear gap, being less prone than rabbits to squeeze through undergrowth. Where rabbit fencing is present, this will aid hare control, but fencing is unlikely to be justified for hares alone.

Mountain (or blue) hares are mostly found on heather moor and mountains, and tend to require longer vegetation for cover than brown hares. In undisturbed heather, their trails (usually running up and down hill) may be conspicuous.

E. Squirrels

i. History and habits

Despite the popular reference to the grey squirrel as the 'tree-rat', the two squirrels found in Britain are closely related. When the grey squirrel was introduced (to over 30 sites between 1876 and 1929), it created the peculiar situation of an introduced animal apparently better adapted to the mainly deciduous and open habitat of modern Britain than its native counterpart. As a result of this introduction, the red squirrel will probably be mostly restricted in future to the large conifer forests to which it is better adapted.

The staple diet of the red squirrel is conifer seed (primarily Scots pine, but also Norway spruce and other species). Green cones become edible for squirrels from around August of their second year until they drop as mature brown cones in spring and summer of the following year. The main shortfall of food (other than in poor cone years) therefore occurs in early summer, which is when squirrels turn to other diet items including the sappy underlayer of tree-bark.

Grey squirrels have a more varied diet which includes the nuts, fruit, mast and seed of broadleaf trees (hazel, oak, beech, elm, horse and sweet chestnuts, sycamore, ash, hornbeam, rowan, hawthorn and others), conifer seed (spruce, pines and larch especially), buds and young shoots in spring, fungi, and other forage from fields and gardens. Tree-bark underlayer is of even greater importance to them than to red squirrels in providing food in the May – July period. Grey squirrels also eat eggs and young from bird nests.

Mature females of both species usually give birth in spring (Feb-early April) and summer (June–July) with an average of 3 young in each litter, though food supply and weather conditions cause fluctuations in this pattern. A large proportion of these young squirrels, however, will not survive their first winter unless they can find a vacancy in suitable woodland habitat. Having evolved in competition with other squirrel species in America, the grey squirrel appears more adept at colonising than the red squirrel, a second major factor in its success in this country.

Squirrels use dreys for shelter, sleep and breeding. The red squirrel's drey is almost invariably situated by the trunk of a mature conifer, and about 250 mm in diameter. Grey squirrel dreys are often built away from the trunk and tend to be large, leafier and (especially during the summer) less compact and tidy. Main periods of squirrel activity occur after sunrise and before sunset, also during better weather conditions. Neither red nor grey squirrel hibernates.

ii. Planning the control programme

Fortunately not all trees in the forest are vulnerable to squirrel damage. Grey squirrels strip the bark of 15-40 year old beech and sycamore by preference. They will also damage 15-40 year old oak, pine (Scots, lodgepole and Corsican), hemlock, ash, larch and birch. Red squirrel damage is principally found on 10-50 year old Scots pine, though other species may be affected (see 'Damage identification', p. 62).

Unfortunately it is not easy to predict which species will be attacked on any given forest, and whether damage will be sufficiently severe to justify control.

The ranger normally considers the following questions:

(1) ***Are squirrel numbers generally high?*** This is normally dependent upon the suitable habitat and availability of food in the surrounding woodland and (especially for grey squirrels) farmland.

(2) ***Have squirrels damaged a certain species in previous years?*** This is the major guideline for predicting in the short-term. If 25 year-old Scots pine comes under attack by greys in one or two parts of a forest, it is reasonable to protect all such plantations for a few years.

(3) ***Have conditions been suitable for an unusual increase in squirrel numbers?*** A good supply of over-wintering food (eg mast and cones), mild winter and dry spring are likely to be followed by an increase in squirrel numbers. Large clear-fells next to vulnerable crops may also concentrate squirrel numbers in the same year.

Some thought about the biology of squirrels should make it clear that it is not desirable, economic or indeed possible to eradicate squirrels in the whole forest. The only reasonable solution to squirrel problems available to us at present is to reduce squirrel numbers immediately prior to and during the damage period (April–July) and only in the immediate vicinity of vulnerable trees. If squirrels are killed at other times and places (say for example in autumn when it is tempting to consider controlling squirrels gathering on mature hardwoods) it will merely mean that more juvenile squirrels will move into the main woods and survive the winter. The same number of squirrels will gather in suitable plantations for bark-stripping the following spring and summer.

Once a pattern of vulnerable species in a given forest has become established, it would be useful to the ranger to obtain a computer print-out each year indicating the compartments most likely at risk.

Squirrel damage can be overlooked. The ranger should search all vulnerable compartments, standing back and looking into the tops of the trees with binoculars.

iii. Grey squirrel control

The accepted and legal methods of controlling grey squirrels are cage-trapping, spring-trapping (provided the spring-trap is of an approved type and sited in a tunnel, see Section 7 C ii), hopper-poisoning with warfarin (provided there are no red squirrels present in the area), and shooting, alone or in combination with drey-poking.

In most circumstances the most efficient methods are cage-trapping and hopper-poisoning with warfarin. The success of both methods depends upon the ranger's ability to find sites on the forest floor which are most regularly used by squirrels. These are invariably where the ground is clear of vegetation, usually on a carpet of dead leaves or needles, often very large hardwoods or yew trees or Scots pines with boughs near the ground, or where a tree has fallen over to provide a runway for squirrels. Sites near to the edge of the forest and adjacent hedgerows are usually also productive. There should be one site approximately every 100-250 metres (in other words every 1-6 hectares), distributed throughout the area of the vulnerable crop and for several hundred metres all round. In relatively small isolated woods it is best to have trapping/poisoning sites throughout the wood.

Traps and hoppers should be pegged or secured firmly to a level area of ground (or else squirrels will undermine traps for the bait, and badgers or even deer will upset the hoppers) then covered and camouflaged with stones, dead wood and turf. This makes them more firmly positioned, and reduces interference from birds, people, badgers, etc.

The third essential point of trapping or poisoning is to get the squirrels feeding hard at these sites by systematic pre-baiting. For at least 5 days before setting the traps several handfuls of maize should be scattered inside the trap and for metres around the site, gradually reducing the amount and bringing it nearer the trap or hopper as the days progress. In the case of traps, the doors should be wedged open during this period. After the fifth day the trap is set and the doors closed, with maize thrown only inside the trap and just outside the swing-door. In case of hoppers, poison is placed in the hoppers immediately and maize is discontinued after pre-baiting. Sites where the pre-bait is not taken must be changed.

Once the traps are set, the ranger needs to carry a sack on his round for extracting squirrels for despatch. Traps must, by law, be visited at least every 24 hours. For the first two days it can be worth making two visits a day. Provided that pre-baiting has been carried out properly, the majority of squirrels are usually caught within the first five to ten days of trapping. One visit a week is normally enough to keep hoppers topped up with poisoned wheat, but it is essential that a continuous supply of poison is available to the squirrels, and where numbers are high it is worth checking hoppers more frequently between the sixth and fifteenth day of poisoning. Once the wheat ceases to be taken it should be removed (and dried and stored for re-use, or disposed of safely, not buried a few inches beneath the surface nearby) even if the hopper is left in situ. This minimises the dangers to other wildlife.

The advantages of cage-trapping are that it provides the ranger with an insight into the squirrel numbers in his area, and it avoids the use of poison. There is no doubt, however, that poison hoppers will achieve the same result with less ranger time. The ranger can usually manage upwards of 50 live-traps per day working full-time on squirrels, where he could manage the same number of hoppers when part of his day is required elsewhere. (This is not to say anyone can position over 50 traps or hoppers a day, because the careful positioning of traps and hoppers is the most important part of the exercise). It is illegal to use warfarin if red squirrels are present.

iv. Red squirrel control

At the end of the last century, red squirrels reached a population peak, and caused considerable damage to mature timber. In recent years such unacceptable damage by red squirrels has been local only, mainly because their populations rarely achieve high densities.

If control does appear necessary, it is essential to realise that the red squirrel is a protected animal (see Section 7 D i), and control may not be carried out except in the circumstances detailed in the 1981 Wildlife and Countryside Act. (See next paragraph, 'Squirrels and the law').

Red Squirrel

v. Squirrels and the law

The red squirrel is protected. Under the terms of the 1981 Wildlife and Countryside Act, control may not be carried out unless (a) it is necessary for the purpose of preventing serious damage, (b) also that as soon as the need for such control becomes apparent, a licence must be applied for from the Ministry of Agriculture. Once the licence has been granted, squirrels can be controlled as indicated by that licence.

Under licence, red squirrels may only be cage-trapped. It is illegal under any circumstances to use spring-traps or poison to kill red squirrels.

Grey squirrels may legally be controlled by (a) shooting, or shooting with drey-poking, (b) spring traps, provided the trap is of an approved type for this species, see Section 7 C ii, (c) warfarin poison, provided the dose of warfarin and the design of the hopper conform to legal requirements (see below, 'Use of warfarin'). It is not legal to use warfarin for the purpose of killing grey squirrels in any area where there is a risk to red squirrels (Wildlife and Countryside Act 1981) or (except inside buildings) in the following counties: Northumberland, Cumberland, Westmorland, Durham, Lancashire, Norfolk, East Suffolk, Isle of Wight, Anglesey, Caernarvon, Denbigh, Flint, Merioneth, Cardigan, Montgomery, Carmarthen. 1973 Grey Squirrels Warfarin Order.

vi. Use of warfarin

(1) Warfarin is a poison! Observe all precautions stipulated on the label of the concentrate bottle.

(2) The ranger should begin with a correctly balanced Warfarin concentrate (0.5% Warfarin concentrate supplied by Killgerm Ltd., P.O. Box 2, Denholme Drive, Ossett, W. Yorkshire, WF5 9NB).

- For squirrels, final bait must not exceed 0.02% mixture, by law. Mix 0.5% concentrate with whole wheat in a 1:24 weight mixture ie ½ kilogram bottle in 12 kilograms wheat.

(3) It is essential to mix the concentrate thoroughly with the wheat in order to produce a legal and effective bait. Place wheat in clear polythene sack, pour on concentrate, and shake vigorously until all the wheat is evenly coloured. Leave for 2-3 hours before use.

(4) For squirrels, bait must be placed in a legal hopper, according to the provisions of the 1973 Squirrels (Warfarin) Order. This must

- have a tunnel not less than 230 mm long, not more than 100 mm internal diameter or square dimension.

- have a container to hold poisoned bait, firmly attached to one end of the tunnel and securely closed when holding poisoned bait so that the bait is accessible only to animals which have entered and passed along the length of the tunnel. Access by an animal to the poisoned bait where tunnel and container meet must be by a gap not more than 20 mm high and no wider than the tunnel.

(5) Hoppers may currently be obtained from: Alpe Thermo Products, 24 Willsbridge Hill, Willsbridge, Bristol, BS15 6EY; Fuller Engineering Ltd, Felcourt, East Grinstead, West Sussex, RH19 2JY; Males, Warners Lane, Selsey, West Sussex, PO20 9EL; RCR-Layson Ltd, 37 Tatton Court, Kingsland Grange, Warrington, Cheshire, WA1 4RR, and their area agents.

(6) Any unused bait should be burned or buried deeply.

(7) It is illegal to use warfarin for controlling grey squirrels if red squirrels are present.

F. Voles

We have seen (Identification of damage Section 3 A 9) that the only damage of economic significance caused by voles is bark-gnawing round the base of young trees in rank grassy plantations. This occurs if field voles reach superabundant numbers, which they do in a three to five yearly cycle in a suitable grassy habitat. As such peak populations are always followed by an automatic decline, the question needs to be asked whether action should be taken to beat up the plantation (preferably with large trees) and to protect with vole guards. The answer usually depends on whether damage is still continuing when discovered, and on whether the plantation is likely to shade out its grass in the near future.

Note to 1994 reprint

The Campaign against Illegal Poisoning of Animals was launched in March 1991 (by MAFF and DoE) and is supported by a wide range of government departments and organisations with interests in farming, gamekeeping and conservation. General leaflets (PB0894 & PB0447) on illegal poisoning can be obtained from MAFF publications, London SE99 7TP. A video is also now available, price £7.00 plus VAT, which highlights the message of how to recognise and react if illegal poisoning is suspected. There is also a Freephone line for reporting of suspected incidents of illegal poisoning. Tel: 0800 321 600.

G. Insects and fungi

The first point about insects and fungi which attack trees is that the ranger is not normally expected to identify them. Secondly he is not normally expected to deal with them either. Both of these jobs are more likely to be carried out by forest staff, often with the assistance of Research Division. On the other hand neither job can be carried out until the problem has been located, and this is where the ranger has a major part to play, especially when he is the only person visiting large areas of the forest. The importance of this job should not be underestimated, as the damage caused by insects and fungi could be greater on some forests than all other forms of damage, and could be prevented by being spotted in its early stages.

What should the ranger be keeping his eyes and ears open for? The answer is 'anything out of the ordinary'. You are more likely to spot something generally wrong with the tree than see the insect or fungus itself first of all. If you are looking across a valley and see an area of trees which appears discoloured, go and investigate. (The first attack of web-spinning larch sawfly in Britain was discovered by a housewife who noticed from her kitchen window the strange glistening of this insects' webs when seen across a valley). If you are walking through a young plantation and see numerous dead or dying plants, don't ignore them just because you know it isn't rabbit or deer damage. Whenever you are in the forest, you should pay special attention to any large group of trees which appears unusual or different from its neighbours of the same species. Look for discoloured or distorted foliage, foliage and shoots which are damaged or have fallen off, patches of bark falling away, wounds in the living bark, or abnormal resin bleeding. Look for unusually large numbers of birds (eg jackdaws, rooks) which may be feeding in the canopy on a plague of insects. Listen for pattering sound caused by the droppings of a caterpillar plague, though you may find it hard to believe this until you have heard it!

The next thing to remember is that you should always mention anything out of the ordinary in the appearance of trees to your forester. If it is only one or two trees which are affected, it may be a trivial problem, but it would be a very foolish forester who criticised you for wasting his time, because it could equally well be a serious problem in its early stages. Research Division never gets tired of identifying tree abnormalities, and they are increasingly looking to the ranger for assistance in locating new attacks and building up their record of common pests.

In time the ranger will learn to identify the common problems which recur on his forest, such as pine weevil or honey fungus, and a few of these are illustrated in the Identification of Damage Section 3 A. You will also come to recognize the characteristic pattern of appearance that each of these types of damage takes. Even so, don't assume with common problems that the attack is not worth reporting, as you may well be the first to spot it that year, and it still needs dealing with. In fact never assume anything, because it is most likely that a number of major tree pests will arrive in Britain during the coming years, and you may be the first person looking at it! As Sherlock Holmes said, it is not enough to look, you must also observe!

H. Domestic stock

The only widespread damage by domestic stock is caused by sheep, though horses, cattle and goats can cause occasional damage. Sheep are frequently more harmful to young plantations than deer, which have often received the blame for the damage caused by sheep. It is, indeed very difficult on occasion to distinguish between sheep damage except by circumstantial evidence, which usually takes the form of wool (in the fences and on the trees), sheep-droppings and slots. Sheep not only browse (and to some extent strip) young trees, but they are also capable of pulling up newly planted trees.

The forester has two lines of defence against sheep: good fences and good relations with neighbouring farmers. Unless the forest fence is in good order, the battle is lost before begun. Not only should fences be well built (especially at their base, see Section 4 G), they must be inspected regularly. This will be one of the ranger's duties, as he is the person who most regularly patrols forest boundaries, especially march fences in remote upland areas. Temporary repair should always be carried out where possible, and can usually be affected with the aid of bailer-twine plus nearby materials. It is essential to make proper repairs and remove sheep from the plantation as quickly as possible, because once sheep become hefted the situation can only be resolved completely by the farmer selling the sheep.

Good relations with surrounding farmers ensures that they are on the forester's side in dealing with this problem. Co-operation between forester and farmer is to the benefit of both parties in the long run, for example with regard to fox and crow control, and clearly the ranger can play an important role in fostering good relations. If co-operation and gentle persuasion have failed, it may be necessary to warn the farmer, to involve the Ministry of Agriculture (or SOAFD in Scotland) and the NFU, and even to impound the offending stock. In severe sheep-problem areas, the Commission may also employ shepherding rangers, but it is an expensive last resort.

I. Birds

Significant damage by blackgame or capercaillie is rarely encountered outside the North-East of Scotland, and even here only where young plantations (principally pine) are being established in prime habitat for these species. For capercaillie this is mature pinewood, whereas blackgame will increase in an area of extensive young plantations. Blackgame will often use plantations (particularly birch trees) as perching places adjacent to lekking grounds. Moreover in healthy plantations, recovery from damage is often so rapid that there is little trace within a few years. Consequently, in view of conservation value of both species, the assumption should be that control is unnecessary. Where this assumption is clearly contradicted by experience, the only effective measure of control is to reduce the population of the offending species in and near the damaged plantation by shooting. This should, of course, only be undertaken in the respective legal seasons. Capercaillie are rather slow recolonizers, so control will rarely need to be repeated. As with deer, the sporting significance of these species as well as their damage potential and conservation significance (see Section 3 H) may be considered where numbers are high.

Large starling roosts can cause a rather unattractive area of damage within the forest, sometimes extending to a hectare or more. Given that moving a roost can be quite difficult and costly, and only cause the problem to be transferred elsewhere, it is often more sensible to tolerate them. If this is impractical, further reference should be made to FC Leaflet 69.

J. Species not harmful to forestry

In some areas the control of foxes and crows (see Section 3 H above, on sheep), and possibly mink, may be an essential part of good neighbourly policy. Otherwise there is no economic or ecological justification for the ranger to control predatory species, whether foxes, mink, crows, stoats, weasels, wild cats, pine martens, polecats or any other. It is, for example, fallacious to imagine that the spread of mink in this country can be prevented. Nevertheless it may be necessary to control mink, which are easily trapped, where they are causing unacceptable damage to wildfowl reserves or fishing interests.

It must be added that where fox control is important, traditional earths or cairns should not be ploughed over at the planting stage, as this will cause the ranger a great deal of lost time and effort.

Section 4
Deer management

A. Introduction

B. Species biology

C. Training and beginning

D. Breeding capacity, census and size of cull

E. Management according to species and habitat

F. Forest design for deer management

G. Fenced plantations

H. High seats and hides

I. Deer and the law

J. Taking the shot

K. Reaction to the shot

L. Following a blood trail

M. Preparing the carcass

N. Preparation of heads and trophies

O. Further considerations

P. Summary

A. Introduction

Since the early 1950s the Forestry Commission has been developing a widely-respected approach to large-scale deer management, based on the pursuit of two fundamental aims: Efficient crop protection (ie scientific management) and the welfare of deer (ie humane management).

Any other management objectives, such as the provision of sporting or production of venison, are always subject to these two primary considerations. Conservation as an aim in itself is rarely necessary, but the provision of amenity may influence the deer management on such well-known wildlife forests as the New Forest, Cannock and Grizedale.

B. Species biology

It is essential to base this efficient and humane deer management upon accurate field-knowledge of the behaviour and biology of the deer themselves. Indeed, we should also consider each species in its historical perspective in order to avoid the assumption sometimes made that an animal is no more than a pest at a given moment of time.

The following illustrated pages give information for five British wild species. This will only provide a framework for the ranger's local knowledge, as in every area deer behave slightly differently according to their surroundings.

Red deer *(Cervus elaphus)*

Originally native to woodland throughout Britain. Now uncommon in the south and lowlands, except in a few forests and woodlands where they have generally survived in association with parks or by re-introduction. In Scotland, by contrast, red deer are extremely numerous, having widely colonised recent plantations from former or adjacent 'deer forest'.

In the field red deer are large, unspotted, and have a creamy rump patch which runs on to the flat of the back and encompasses a short tail (contrast with sika). When disturbed they move with a distinctive gliding trot. Stags are usually distinguishable after 9 months of age by pedicles and antlers, thicker necks, deeper chests, position of ears (more horizontal than hinds). Further distinguishable characteristics of age and condition in Chapter O.

Red deer are sociable, living in groups for most of the year, but in common with other non-territorial species of deer, the mature males (usually of 3 years and over) live separate lives for most of the year, away from the family parties led by mature hinds. Immature and yeld hinds may also form a third group. In the Highlands, stags may be found near or even below the hinds in winter (both groups move downhill in severe weather), but in summer they are usually on the highest grazings. In woodlands the family groups are usually found on the main central areas of forest, with the stags tending to live in outlying

Red deer

areas. A fundamental distinction must be drawn between the biology of hill deer and of forest-living deer. Forest deer are capable of far higher rates of reproduction (and therefore require much higher culls) because the food and especially the shelter in their habitat is so much better. The highest densities of deer occur in thicket stage crops, which is when the combined advantages of food and shelter are at their best. Forest-living deer live in much smaller groups, typically from 2 to 5 together, and not 20, 50 or sometimes a hundred which is typical of hill deer. The hind groups of forest-living deer have smaller home-ranges on which they remain throughout the year.

From the second half of September the stags join the hind groups which have begun to gather in traditional rutting areas. The location of these areas can vary depending upon food availability eg between good and bad mast years. During the rut large stags attempt to hold as many hinds as possible in a group away from other stags. Fights may be severe. Single calves are born in late May/June, and should lose their spotted coats by or before September. Poor calves show harsh, gingery coats and appear short in the body. Late calves are at a permanent disadvantage.

Individual hinds (especially on hungry forests) may have barren or 'yeld' years, during which time they regain breeding condition. Much of the other behaviour of red deer, such as antler growth, wallowing and fraying, is closely related to this seasonal reproductive rhythm of the two sexes, as shown in the calendar below. The normal life span of red deer is 16-18 years.

Male	Stag
Female	Hind
Young	Calf
Male	2nd year - brocket
	3rd year - spire
	4th year - staggart
	5th year - stag
Male	Hummel - without antlers
Male	Switch - clean beam no points
Male	Royal - 12 points
Male	Imperial - 14 points
Male	Monarch - master stag
Non-breeding hind	Yeld hind
Voice of stag in rut	Roar or bellow
Group	Herd

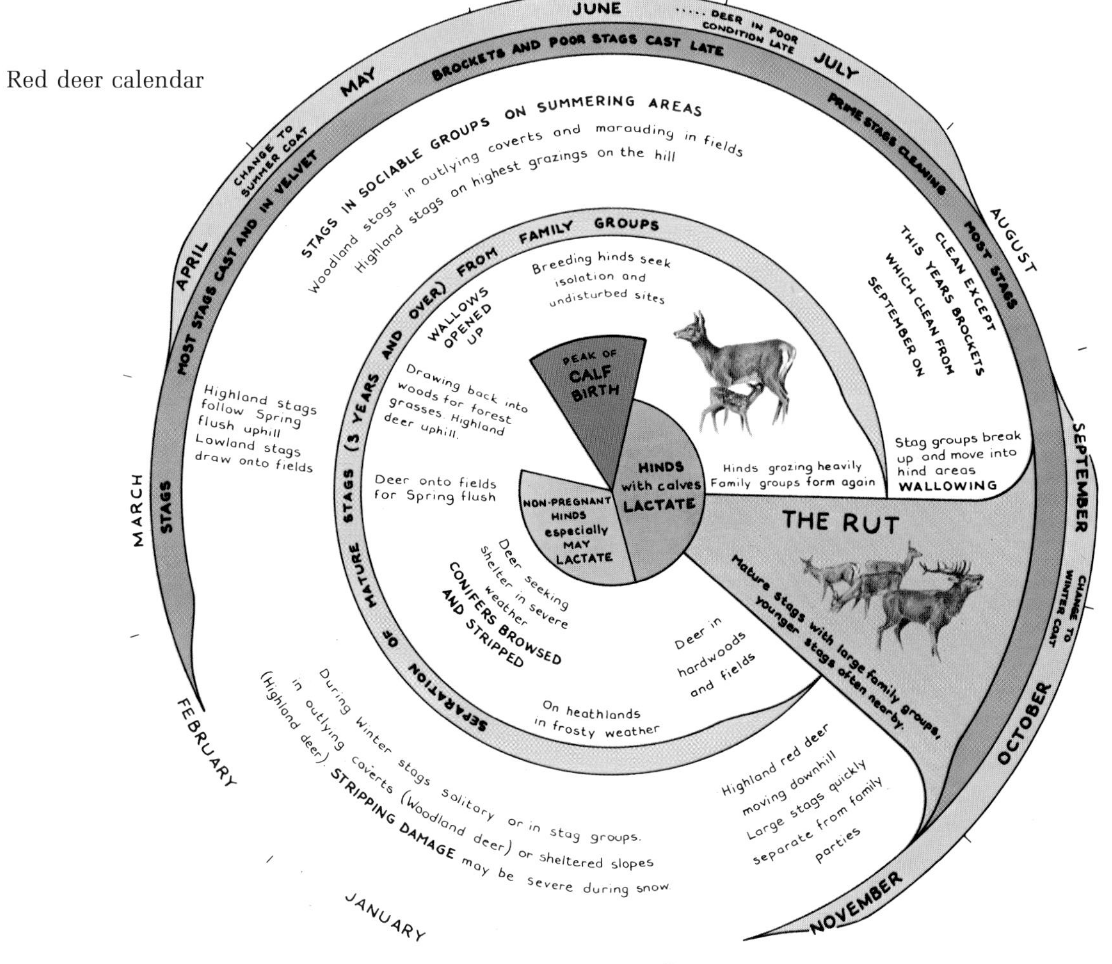

Red deer calendar

Sika deer *(Cervus nippon)*

Introduced to Britain and Ireland during the second half of the nineteenth century, mostly via Powerscourt Park (Co Wicklow), but it is not known exactly which strains of deer were imported. The position is complicated by the presently-held belief that only Japanese (and possibly Taiwanese) sika are pure wild species, the other forms resulting from ancient hybridisation with eastern wapiti. What is certain is that the sika which have gone wild in several parts of Britain and Ireland are capable of hybridisation with red deer, and in some cases this has already taken place. The purity of the native red deer stocks of Britain is therefore considerably threatened by the spread of sika in the wild.

In the field pure sika are distinctive from red deer. In particular the coat changes dramatically from a bright spotted chestnut in summer to a charcoal grey/brown in winter, hinds being less dark than stags. At close quarters the scent-glands on the rear legs are distinctly white on sika, and more prominent. (This feature often betrays red deer look-alike hybrids). The heart-shaped rump patch does not run on to the flat of the back, the hairs of the patch are fluffed out more obviously in alarm, and the tail is longer. Facial markings normally give the deer a distinctive 'sika frown'. Stag's antlers have brow tines running more upright from the main beam, brow and beam are joined by a ridge, and there is usually a maximum of four tines on each antler. Sika have a wider vocal range than all other species of deer in Britain, including the distinctive whistle of the rutting stag (for an interesting detailed account, see S. Smith *Deer* magazine, March 1984). Sika are usually fallow-sized, but stockier and deeper in the body.

There is much work yet to be done on the behaviour of sika. Their general behaviour appears to be very similar to the red deer pattern, with the sexes living apart for most of the year. If anything they prefer denser cover than red deer, often on damp or poorly-drained soils, and preferably in association with good grazing. Like red deer they are grazers rather than browsers, and may be seen in broad daylight on fields if undisturbed, nonetheless heather, conifers and other evergreens are important food items in winter. Most significantly they are capable of serious stripping damage to trees. As yet there is less evidence of their adaptation to moorland except as a secondary habitat to woodland. In early stages of conifer woods they are capable of building their numbers up to high densities.

Stags cast from late March onwards, and as with other species mature animals cast first. At this time of year stags have been seen together in large groups on their favourite areas. In September stags return to the hind areas and, like red deer, indulge in wallowing as part of the build-up to the rut. Most calves are born singly at the end of May/early June. Hinds apparently live in small family groups like woodland reds. Sika have an average life span of 12-14 years.

Male	Stag
Female	Hind
Young	Calf
Voice of Stag	Whistle, shriek
Group	Herd

Sika deer

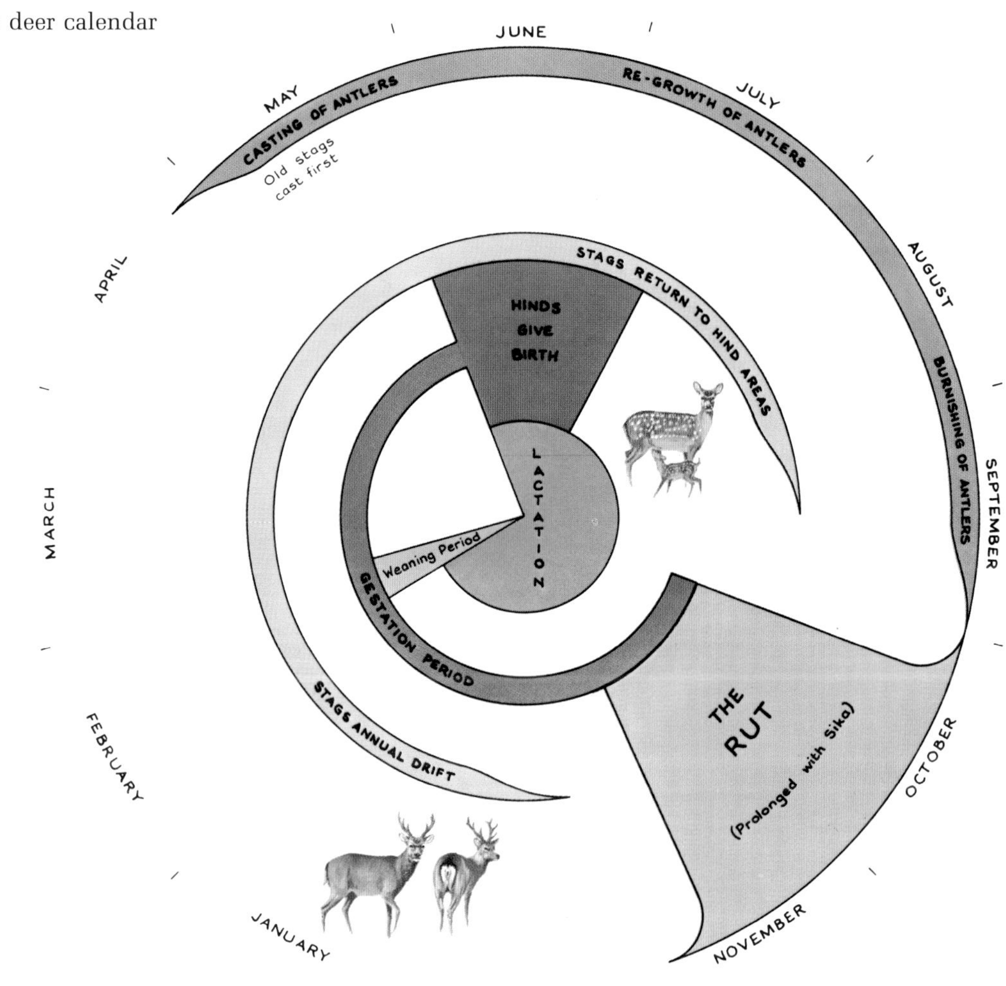

Sika deer calendar

Roe deer *(Capreolus capreolus)*

Native to Britain (not Ireland), but virtually restricted to Scotland by the eighteenth century. Since then has re-established itself as a result of introduction and re-afforestation, and is presently fast expanding its range.

In the field roe deer are small, and have (especially in winter) distinctive white or buff 'target' (rump patch of roe deer) and appear tailless. Adults unspotted, in summer foxy red, in winter dark grey, often with pale throat patches. Black and white muzzle distinctive, as also antlers, if present. Bounding run and alarm bark characteristic. Doe usually distinguishable (especially in winter) by anal hair tuft known as 'tush', though this may not be clear on yearling does though these can always be distinguished by their slender necks.

Roe deer, unlike red, fallow and sika, are largely unsociable and territorial. Adult roe does, once established, will stay on their own area for several years, and will not tolerate other does in this area during the warmer half of the year at least. The territory of the adult buck is usually larger than that of the doe, and frequently overlaps more than one doe territory. Bucks begin to relax their intolerance of one another soon after the rut, and during severe weather all deer may share the best feeding grounds, especially after prolonged snow cover. (Such winter gatherings are known as 'bevies' of roe deer). In the spring, however, juvenile roe are driven into less favourable habitats or, if available, on to uncolonised areas.

The preferred habitat of breeding adults is woodland with areas of dense cover, though other nearby habitats such as moorland and fields are usually exploited seasonally. Roe are browsers rather than grazers by preference. Their requirements are particularly well provided for in the young dense stages of forest plantations.

Roe bucks have a different antler cycle from all other British deer, growing them during winter rather than the summer. The rut is early (late July/early August) but kids (usually twins) are not born until the following May/June as a result of delayed implantation. Kids should lose their spots by October. The false rut is an apparent resurgence of sexual and territorial behaviour by some deer in and around October, but its significance is not fully understood. Roe deer live for 7-10 years.

Male	Buck	Voice of buck and doe	Bark
Female	Doe	Voice of doe in rut	Whistle
Young	Kid	Group	Bevy
Male	2nd year - gazelle 3rd year - hemuse 4th year - fair buck		

Roe deer

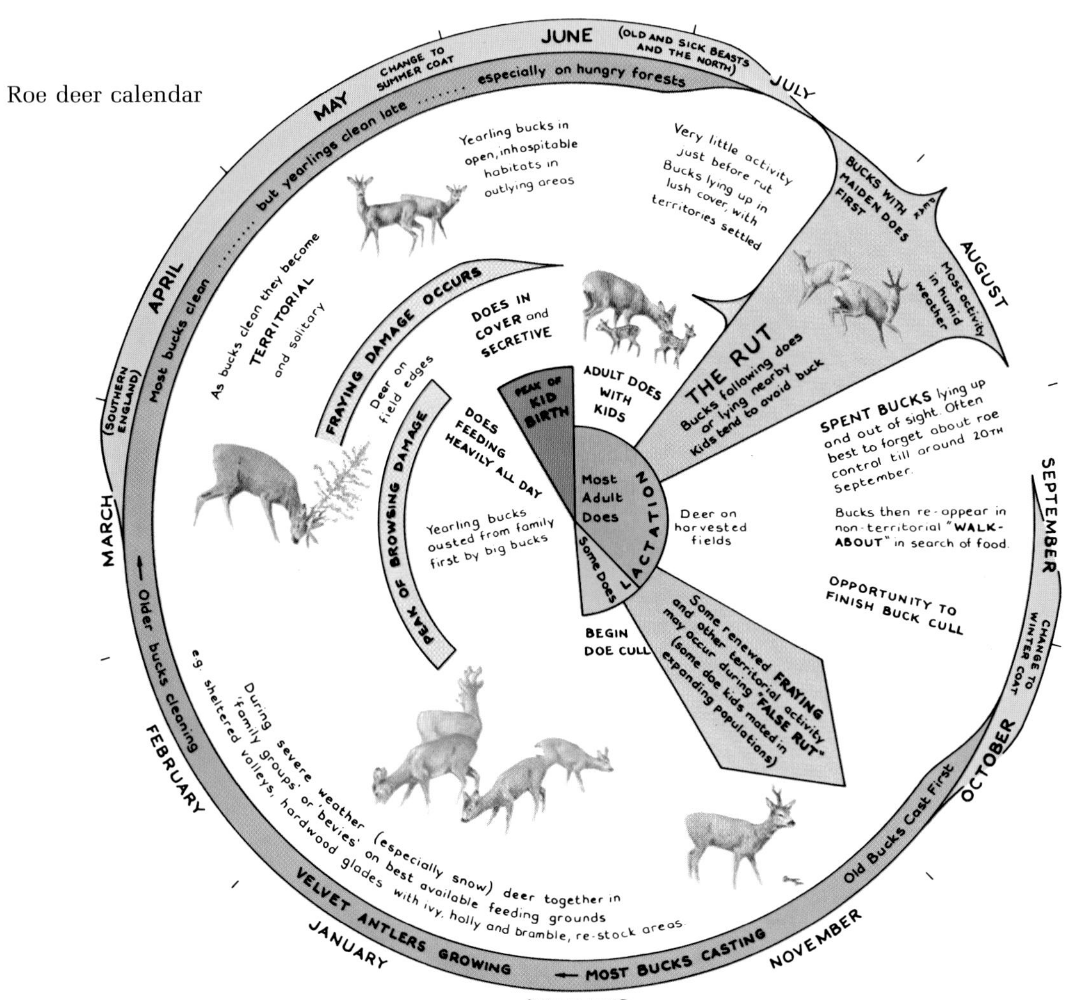

Roe deer calendar

Fallow deer *(Dama dama)*

Introduced to Britain by the Normans, principally as a park animal capable of good breeding performance on poor (especially dry) soils, but also quickly established in the wild on the numerous chases and historical forests. With the recent destruction of many deer parks, it has become further established in several forest plantations. Fallow have a similar life span to sika of 12-14 years.

Medium-sized, elegant deer, very variable in colour. Typical form spotted in summer, grey/brown and white beneath in winter, but darker forms equally common, and whites and menils (brightly spotted form, usually in winter as well) occur in several herds. Long tail (with a black stripe in the common variety) characteristic. Bucks usually distinguishable by pedicles from about 8 months of age, and by very prominent 'brush' of hair on penis sheath from first autumn, also palmated antlers of older deer, more horizontal ears than does.

Fallow deer are frequently more sociable than any other British species, living in groups for most of the year, with bucks living separate lives away from the does and followers, except where their movement is restricted by lack of colonisable ground. Young bucks usually leave with the older bucks at 18 months, though some leave in their third year.

Fallow deer favour open feeding grounds, where large groups (several dozen and more) will gather and remain all day if they are sheltered and undisturbed. Relatively tolerant of human proximity.

In severe weather (especially prolonged snow cover) deer become more restricted to sheltered woodland with good browse and hardwood bark (especially elm). Doe groups prefer the security of larger tracts of woodland or heathland near central parts of the herd's range, while bucks appear to exploit richer feeding grounds (thick cover and agricultural fields) in the outlying areas.

In September and early October bucks begin to return to the doe areas, and both sexes group on traditional rutting sites which are dominated by the largest bucks by dint of great expenditure of energy. It is not unusual to see as many as up to twelve lesser bucks around the rutting stand. Rut finishes in early November, most fawns (usually single) born in June. Large bucks cast in April/May, prickets not until June, most animals clean late August/early September.

Male	Buck
Female	Doe
Young	Fawn
Male	2nd year - pricket
	3rd year - sorel
	4th year - sore
	5th year - bare buck
	6th year - buck
	7th year - great buck
Female	2nd year - yearling
Voice of buck in rut	Groan
Group	Herd

Fallow deer

Fallow deer calendar

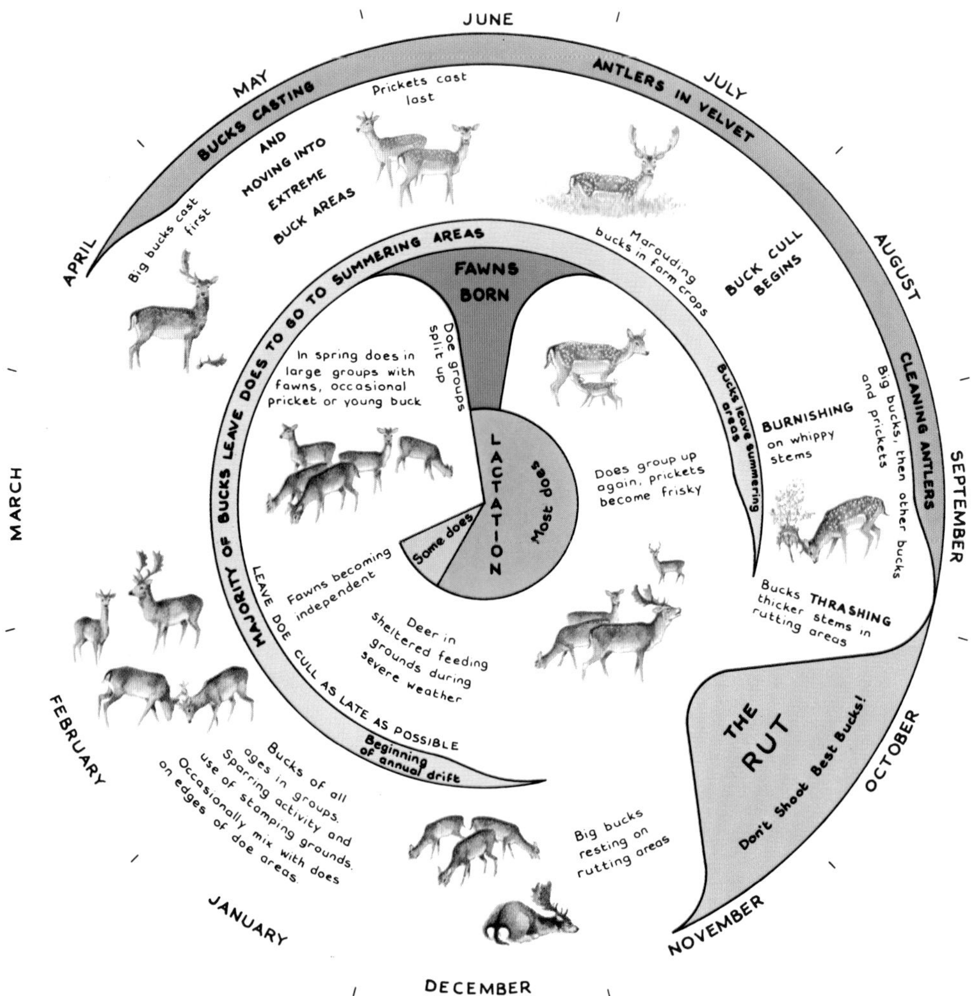

Muntjac (Reeves muntjac, barking deer. *Muntiacus reevesi*)

In the field muntjac are very small (fox-sized), round-backed, and low-slung at the forward end (head, neck and shoulders). The coat is chestnut in summer (May to October approximately), kidney-coloured in winter, usually with touches of ginger. In alarm flight, which is very rapid, the long tail is held aloft, revealing a flared white rump patch. Males are stockier, and have a V-marking on the head produced by the long raked-back pedicles, but antlers are very small (75 mm) and simple. Unlike the other four species of deer muntjac (and Chinese water deer) have a set of canine teeth situated in the upper jaw.

Muntjac are native of mountainous country in south-east Asia. They were introduced to Woburn Abbey around 1900, and have become strongly established in the wild despite the fact that they do not breed seasonally. Doe produces her first fawn at about 18 months of age, and will usually produce one fawn at about 7-8 monthly intervals. Fawn loses spots around 3-4 months.

By contrast male muntjac are seasonal in their antler cycle. Cast May/June, usually clean August/September. Cleaning of antlers accompanied by heightened territorial behaviour and fraying as in other species. Male muntjac seen in velvet at other times of year are believed to be juveniles, born unseasonally, growing first head.

Muntjac become established in dense cover such as thickets of birch, blackthorn, briar and honeysuckle, young forest plantations and woodlands with coppice hazel, bramble undercover and wet areas. Such habitat often occurs on fairly heavy or fertile soils. Less suitable habitat is mostly only colonised by non-breeding juveniles.

Mature, breeding does live in constant territories throughout the year, and will occupy the same area for several years. Bucks occupy larger territories which may overlap the areas of several does. Deer are only observed in larger groups on communal feeding grounds (usually open fields) in winter. Because of their mutual intolerance and fast breeding-rate, muntjac are capable of rapid colonisation of new areas, and where new areas are not available there will be a reserve of non-territorial juveniles.

They are capable of damaging most young tree species, particularly by fraying (see 'Identification of damage' Section 3). Other signs are: slots, small scrapes, large piles of fumits which appear to be territorial boundary markers and well delineated runs. Distinctive loud bark, repeated at brief intervals for up to ¾ hour, by females in breeding condition.

Male	Buck
Female	Doe
Young	Fawn
Voice of buck and doe	Bark
Group	Family group appearance

Muntjac deer

Muntjac calendar

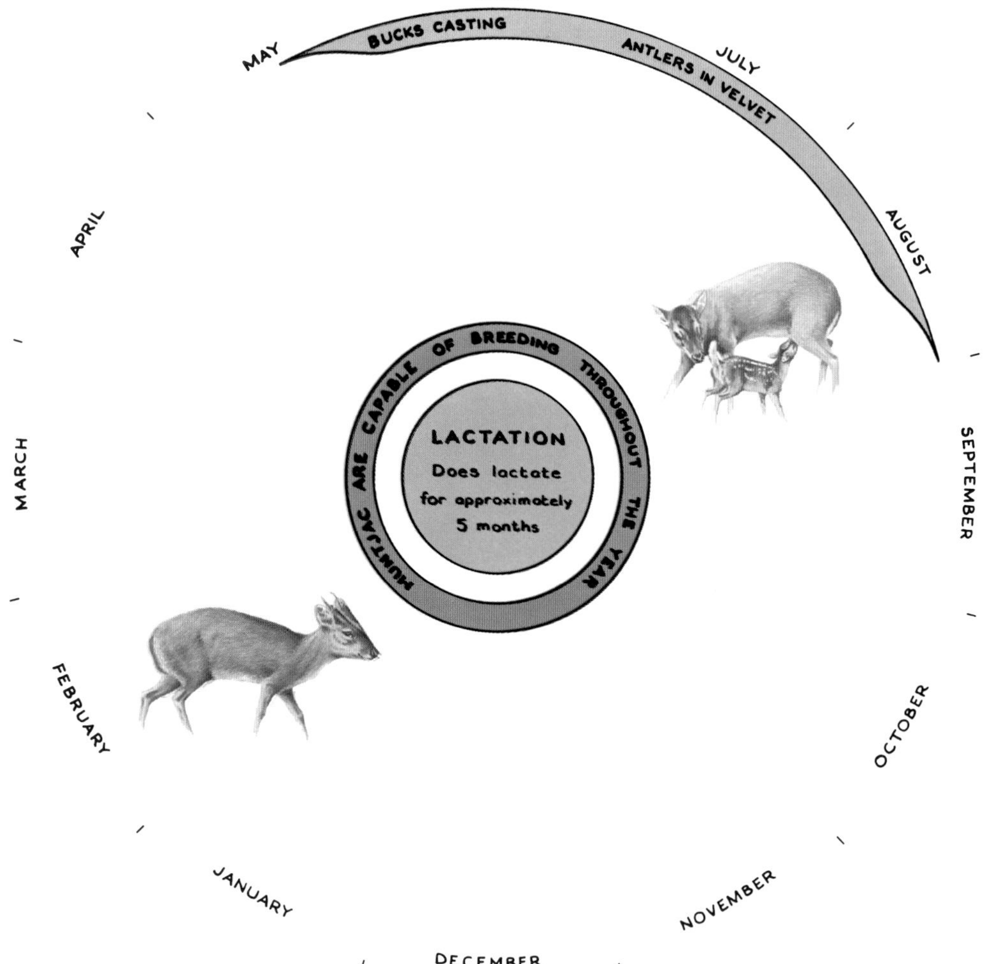

C. Training and beginning

The normal method of deer control is by rifle. Any Forestry Commisssion ranger who undertakes deer control must be trained and approved in the possession and use of the deer-rifle. The principles of rifle possession and use are detailed in chapters of this handbook ('Basic skills', Section 3; 'Taking the shot', later this section; 'The ranger and the law', Section 7) which are intended to remind the ranger of his training. They are not to be treated as a substitute for training.

The first management step to be taken in most forests is for the ranger to meet foresters, landowners, farmers, gamekeepers and any other people with a direct interest in the area on which deer are to be managed, including the previous ranger or deer-manager. These meetings will achieve a double purpose. Firstly, they will teach the ranger a great deal about the limitations and scope of the deer management plan he must undertake. Secondly, they will begin the process of establishing all-important personal contacts upon which the success of the plan will partly depend.

At the same time the ranger begins to walk his forest to get to know the deer. In particular, he should try to discover areas specially well favoured by deer, damage to forest and farm crops (see Section 3), main deer routes to and from feeding areas where deer may be seen at dawn and dusk, resting-up areas and (according to species) major rutting stands, stamping grounds and wallows, as well as paths and glades which he himself can stalk with a good chance of seeing deer. It is often helpful to the ranger to record all this information on a map.

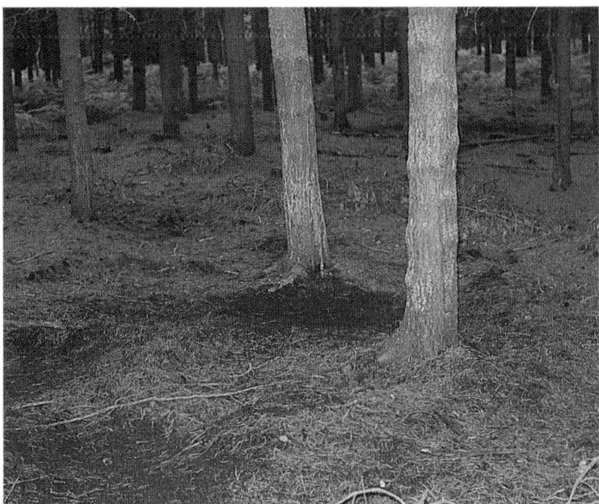

Fallow deer scrape at rutting stand

D. Breeding capacity, census and size of cull

It is never enough to kill deer in response to damage. Where deer populations exist in large-scale forests (especially red deer in Scotland, and roe deer generally) such an approach simply does not work. The only correct and successful way to deal with deer damage is to prevent it reaching unacceptable levels in the first place. And the only way to do this is by means of scientific management. In practical terms this means it is essential to be able to predict the development of your forest in terms of habitat (especially age and species of tree, extent of accessibility of forest), which determines the size and breeding capacity of the deer population, and in terms of the size of cull needed to manage deer at a steady level which does not cause excessive damage.

On very large forests, some of this work may need to be carried out with the aid of the Forestry Authority's Research Division. Forestry Commission Bulletin 71 *Management of Red Deer in Upland Forests* (P R Ratcliffe, 1987) and Bulletin 105 *Roe Deer Biology and Management* (P R Ratcliffe and B A Mayle, 1992) provide further useful information.

On smaller areas of forest it is still important to consider the effects of changing habitat (is the forest going into a thicket stage, which is known to be the best habitat for deer resulting in increased numbers?) and to monitor breeding success. However, it is usually possible to rely on the following more conventional methods to obtain figures for the annual census in April.

Census is best obtained by estimates resulting from observations by the ranger throughout the year, though on some forests a more formal system may be in effect. By any system deer numbers are almost invariably underestimated.

With herding deer the ranger will naturally take advantage of the times of year when deer tend to show in large groups in the open, and the main male and female groups may be observed separately (February-May). At this time of year it is also helpful to consider the effect of the preceding cull (all known deaths) on the size of the herd. Further observations may be made during the rut, plus careful consideration of the estimated number of yearling males (prickets or brockets), which provide a good indicator of the previous year's natural increase.

With territorial species (roe, muntjac) or any species in unbroken forest, a multiplication of estimated density x area may also be useful.

The size of the cull should be aimed quite simply at maintaining the deer at a level which does not lead to unacceptable crop damage. If effective deer control is taking place, all known deaths should usually amount to at least 30% of the April census, and far higher with roe deer - probably 50% or more.

During the year it may be necessary to raise cull figures to respond to damage or an under-estimate in the census figures, the reverse adjustment is rarely necessary.

The sex ratio of the cull will generally be in the region of 1:1 but urgent population reductions are achieved by concentrating on the female cull. The female cull is of paramount importance in roe control and the ratio of male to female cull is nearer 1:2. Even where deer have colonised a forest recently, and they are not yet overnumerous, it is sensible to begin to establish culling and management patterns.

E. Management according to species and habitat

We can now understand why the different species should be managed very differently, and even the same species requires different management techniques in different habitats.

(i) Red and sika deer

Red deer are usually not difficult to control in the relatively small and accessible woodlands in the southern half of Britain, though problems may arise in containing the movements of these wide-ranging animals in such small-scale countryside. In these situations red and sika deer management depends upon agreement over areas on which the hinds in particular can lead a settled life, and upon prompt response to complaints from farmers, along with reasonable provision of deer glades. This system of management is detailed further in the paragraph below on fallow deer.

The problems more usually associated with red deer management arise in the extensive forests with poor access in the north. The red deer in these forests are able to survive in sufficient numbers to cause severe tree damage (principally stripping, also browsing, see Section 3 A), without ever needing to appear in areas where they can be culled adequately to control their numbers. The solution is to open and provide access to sites where deer may be culled efficiently, and the details given in the following chapter on forest design are especially appropriate to red deer. This problem of control is increasing in modern large-scale plantations, and goes a long way to explaining why the Forestry Commission has needed to develop the techniques of deer management.

Particularly serious damage can arise in woodlands which are situated near to extensive open deer forest. These woodlands are inevitably subject to invasion by non-resident (so-called marauding or invading) deer, especially during severe snowy winter weather when the deer seek shelter from the open moorland. In the balance between good neighbour policy and protection of its own crops, the Commission usually seeks to solve this problem by joint action with neighbours and in Scotland with the Red Deer Commission on improved perimeter fences containing down falls and jump-outs. Where marauding deer are still causing unacceptable damage, revised culls become necessary. Glades may need to be kept clear on the inside of the perimeter fence, or in locations where these deer are most likely to appear. (See also 'Deer fencing').

The preference of sika deer for damp valley sites and dense cover adjacent to grazing will influence the choice of deer glades for this species. Sika (and also red deer) may usually be culled on surrounding agricultural fields where these are present.

(ii) Roe deer

Damage by roe deer, which is principally to young trees in the form of browsing and fraying, can also be a serious problem. The difficulty with roe deer is that the deer culled in the vicinity of young plantations are quickly replaced, many times over, from the reserve of other deer living in less favourable habitats in the forest and surrounds. For this reason, many culls which have been undertaken in the past, although appearing quite adequate in view of the number of deer believed to be present, have not really been effective at all in terms of crop protection. The problem is obviously at its worst in large forests with poor access, and also where windthrow is a factor, with the resulting roots and stumps to help the deer and hinder the stalker.

Where roe damage is a problem, the following points should be considered:

a) On established forests, the larger the area of clear fell and resulting new plantation in one place, the easier it is to protect young trees, because time and money spent creating and using a high seat and glades becomes justified. Areas of 15-25 hectares are optimal.

b) Although emphasis, in both forest design and ranger time, should be directed towards the young plantation areas, culling should not be neglected in any part of the forest.

c) On newly established forests, it is essential to leave aside the best deer glades from the outset.

d) The best roe deer glades (in addition to seats and rides around young plantations) are often fairly large areas (¾<2 hectares) in sheltered, fertile valley sites. Glades at the smaller end of this range can be laid out like a chain of beads. Old hardwoods are ideal as the forest becomes more mature. Well-favoured glades of this nature will be used, like large areas of clear fell, as non-territorial grounds by deer gathering from a large surround. This is particularly so in the winter months, and therefore assists the next point.

e) The doe cull is more important than the buck cull where control is a problem.

f) Where control is a problem, culling should not be restrained by ideas of selection. In these situations the priority is not to produce good trophies, and in any case the best way to do so is to keep the population low. Quantity is the enemy of quality.

g) Nor is the theory of not culling territorial animals justified in control problem areas. The removal of an established buck or doe from a convenient deer glade will provide the opportunity of seeing one or more colonising deer during the following days, and therefore keep the cull moving. The even-spectrum cull which will result from a non-selective policy is as humane and beneficial to the deer as any other, if not more so.

h) Where control is a problem, the ranger should not turn down opportunities to cull deer in season. Trophy bucks should not be passed over with the intention of keeping them for licensed stalkers.

(iii) Fallow deer

From the control and management point of view, fallow offer the great advantage of the deer that think collectively, so that the main herd may be encouraged or discouraged on certain areas. The best fallow management in forestry therefore entails:

a) The establishment of culling and sanctuary areas. Sanctuary areas are chosen where deer are appreciated by the general public or private landowners, and where they are safe from persecution. Culling takes place on the rest of the herd area, with particular emphasis in the vicinity of vulnerable crops, unsympathetic neighbours (bearing in mind how much time fallow will spend in fields), dangerous roads and vulnerable situations for persecution of deer. In addition, permission

should be sought by the ranger to cull deer on surrounding fields to reduce agricultural crop damage, except on fields (especially grass but also cereals, rape, etc) included within a sanctuary.

b) It is also essential to establish sanctuaries on the ground which the deer themselves have chosen, if the plan is to succeed. Does and fawns have a preference for fairly secure sites near the centre of the herd's main range, though often in fairly open and even public access areas if these are extensive, eg heathland, open woodland with adjacent grass-fields. Bucks on the other hand seek dense cover in spring and summer, usually towards the edge of the deer range and in striking distance of field crops. The establishment of the doe sanctuary is both easier and more important, nonetheless a suitable buck sanctuary within the forest will be helpful to management, and it is also in the interest of stable management not to shoot large bucks on the major rutting stands. During severe weather both sexes seek shelter and food combined, typically bramble in woodland, as do other species.

c) The advantage of this system is that it simultaneously provides good crop protection and an unharassed way of life for the deer by the imposition of a framework of stability. If the system is to work, it must be carried out with long-term consistency. Even though this will sometimes mean some localised crop damage, this must be weighed against the overall advantage.

(iv) Muntjac

Damage by muntjac is principally to young trees through browsing and fraying. Damage is rarely as severe as roe deer damage, but where it is considered necessary to cull muntjac, the following points of management should be considered:

(a) The key to efficient rifle control of muntjac is to disturb deer (at any time of the day) to increase the number crossing well-mown rides. A well-trained slow dog to move deer from thick cover is essential. This may be done by one ranger moving deer before sitting up, or by two rangers working in conjunction. It requires some skill and experience for two rangers to work together safely in this way. Wide, well-mown rides are important.

(b) A particular difficulty arises with the doe cull, which is the most important in reducing numbers, as muntjac does may just have given birth at any time of year. A more humane method of control in this respect would be to net deer, so that does heavy with milk could be released. Until this becomes a legal alternative, however, rangers can attempt to distinguish pregnant and lactating does, or cull does accompanied by well-grown fawns, but neither suggestion in practice is infallible.

F. Forest design

A vital management step to be taken on any forest is for the ranger and forester to co-operate in making sure that the ranger can undertake control efficiently to guard against unacceptable crop damage. The key to this is to open up and link together, as cheaply as possible, those areas which most benefit deer management. This process is known as forest design. The more difficult it is to see deer in a forest, the more urgent the need for forest design to permit effective control.

The following notes give a guide to the process of selecting and developing deer management areas (known as deer glades). They are applicable both to designing new plantations (when selected glades may be marked and left unploughed), and improving established plantations, and redesigning plantations following clearfelling (and windthrow) before replanting. The latter is particularly important today with so many forests approaching their second rotation.

Rides and paths – The first priority is often to link together existing areas on which deer may be seen, to enable the ranger to move from one such area to another in a continuous stalk, and make a quiet approach.

- Small stalking paths can follow deer paths in the forest or on old deer range to be planted. Deer seem to accept this arrangement where public access is low. The ends of paths should be left concealed.
- Fell young trees or brash to allow at least free passage with rifle in wet weather.
- Bend direction of paths periodically, or even widen them to reach areas of good keep, eg bramble, good grass. (In some cases this may also break up the line of these paths for visual considerations).
- Paths do need maintenance. Or may be developed if successful into larger rides.
- Clear out any suitable existing rides, leaving occasional clumps of cover and improved browse (rowan, willow, birch, etc, in upland forests). This work is usually done with a clearing saw if there is no tractor accessibility.

Old hardwoods – any surviving patches of mature broadleaves or mixed species appear to be most attractive to deer, especially in moorland and young conifer environments and especially lower down hillsides and in conjunction with streamsides. They obviously offer the right combination of cover, shelter, sweet grasses and browse, plus mast in autumn/winter. Patches of old hardwoods are often ready-made and self-maintaining deer glades.

Streamsides and flushes – these are similarly very attractive to deer for good grasses and browse, also for fresh water and mud.

- Followed or crossed by deer moving up and downhill morning and evening.
- Associated with wallows on banks.
- Worth opening up brooks previously planted to their edges.

Grassy clearings – well-used browse and grassy patches on the most fertile ground are worth leaving in new plantations, or clearing inside established plantations where they may be associated with heavily browsed trees. It is usually more sensible to maintain such damaged areas (by pruning if necessary) as glades, than attempt to replant them, as they have been selected by the deer.

- In some large upland forests, old valley farmland left unplanted inside the forest fence provides the most productive form of deer glade, which may in some cases be fairly extensive.
- In lowland forests where rides can be swiped easily to support grass, grassy rides will be a major feature of deer management.

Preferably swiped on a 2-yearly rotation, as shown in Section 2, to produce browse species as well.

Heath and moorland – rank heather is best for deer. In snow-cover it provides an alternative food to tree-bark, and is a laying-up site in summer.

● Inside some extensive upland forests, resident deer may only appear in the open on remote heathery clearings inside the forest. These can be adapted to serve as glades by providing access.

Other sites – wallows, stamping grounds and salt-licks are important to the ranger as indicators of deer activity and worth keeping open and linking into the stalking paths even if not used for culling.

● High-seats and hides looking out across hillsides are an important part of the forest design system. See 'High seats' on the following pages.

● Crossing-places near feeding sites can be as productive, in terms of culling, as the feeding areas themselves.

General considerations – shelter and fertility of ground are paramount in the choosing of glades. There is no merit in just developing existing rides if these are not already favoured.

● Safety for shooting eg dished rather than domed hillsides.

● Access for extraction is a third essential consideration.

● Deer glades should be distributed over all areas of the forest used by deer, at a suggested density of 2-3 per 100 hectares, normally in the ¼<2 hectare range, but occasionally larger on good sites (eg old farmland), or in linear form (eg path with small glades ie 'chain of beads', or burnside).

● Flexibility in trying, abandoning and adapting deer glades is important. On the other hand it is equally important not to abandon successful glades.

● Planning ahead with deer glades (especially before ploughing and planting during afforestation) is easier and more effective than dealing with the problem as it arises.

Improved grass-management – established successful glades may be enhanced by re-seeding and fertilising. However it is not worth re-seeding unless the seed-mix is suitable to the site, and the more productive and palatable grasses and legumes sown are maintained afterwards by improved and consistent management. In several instances improved management alone will have the desired effect, encouraging palatable grasses and legumes in the original sward.

Management measures include: regular fertilising (eg with lime, potash, phosphate, slurry, farmyard manure, trace elements, etc); mowing to maintain low grasses; letting in sunshine or improving shelter of a glade.

G. Fenced plantations

The use of deer-fencing to protect plantations is increasingly being considered as both uneconomic and unsuccessful in many situations. (See FC Bulletin 102). Nevertheless, it is clearly justified in the case of very vulnerable plantations (eg hardwoods, and plantations with high risk of invasion by hill deer), and the ranger should consider the following points on using a deer-fence to best advantage.

(i) The weakest points in any fence are the gate and the bottom wire. Inspection gates should be built into the top half of a deer fence to minimise the possible entry by deer if accidentally left open. Gates for vehicle access should have strong hinges and a lock, and also be fitted in such a way that the gate will naturally swing shut if left alone. It is most inadvisable to leave gates open during the day and only shut them at night. The lower high tensile strainer-wire of a fence must be as close to the ground level as possible. Any gaps under the fence due to rough ground must be blocked by rails or

extra netting or, if appropriate, a water gate. It is useful to line the bottom of the fence with brash, if available.

(ii) A fence should not be erected with standing trees inside, as they provide cover for deer.

(iii) The fence-line should not be within a tree length of standing trees, as these may fall on the fence in storms.

(iv) To avoid large numbers of deer entering plantations the ranger should regularly patrol the fence-line (especially of a new enclosure) at least once a week. Any gaps under the fence must be plugged with brash or stones or whatever is at hand; watergates must be cleared; after heavy or drifting snow always check for tracks inside the fence; always carry your rifle with you.

(v) When deer get inside the enclosure, as they will, especially during the first 12 months, they must be shot immediately (ie within days) before they become 'hefted' to the area and cease travelling the fence-line, otherwise they will be far more difficult to find. It is pointless to try and drive deer out of an enclosure, they must be shot, if necessary out of season.

Deer which are no longer running the fence are best dealt with by placing reliable rifles at suitable points and moving the deer (especially roe) with a well-trained, persistent dog. Clearly by this stage a quick, humane kill is important, not a 'sporting stalk'.

If the deer bursts out of the fence, all well and good, merely repair the hole. If it goes to ground in a heap of brash, it is often necessary to abandon the job until the next day, as it can be extremely difficult for the dog to find any scent.

H. High seats and hides

High seats are not always the most productive method of deer stalking, but they are usually the safest. They undoubtedly have a place when taking out permit stalkers (see Section 6 A), in the control of roe and muntjac, and in the control of larger species in suitable circumstances (usually high density populations in predominantly thicket-stage crops, and in areas of high public access).

The siting of permanent high-seats is critical, and one of the arts in which the ranger slowly acquires experience. Overlooking an edge between thicket-stage crops and feeding grounds (eg grass rides, young plantation, bramble area etc) is usually successful; alternatively fifty to one hundred metres (according to species) back from feeding ground, overlooking rides which deer must cross especially when travelling towards them in the evening.

Where conditions are less conducive to siting permanent high seats, a strong, rust-proof portable seat may be a success. A portable seat is also useful when choosing sites for permanent seats.

High seats being sited for observation rather than control purposes (mostly for deer watching by the public on suitable forests) must of course overlook sanctuary areas on which deer are never or rarely shot. Such seats, often called 'belvederes', are built to a higher standard of comfort, appearance and capacity than usual.

All high seats on the forest must be built to a safe standard with regard to suitably strong materials, and correctly reinforced ladders. There are almost as many designs for high seats as rangers, but the following design can serve as a suggestion. See also Forestry Commission Leaflet 74, 'High Seats for Deer Management'.

High seats, both portable and permanent, have been developed for use in flat or gently undulating country but there are circumstances where the structure of a hide built at ground level is equally effective for either control or observation. The same criteria apply to the siting of such structures but their cost is usually less, both in terms of labour, materials and subsequent maintenance. Such structures

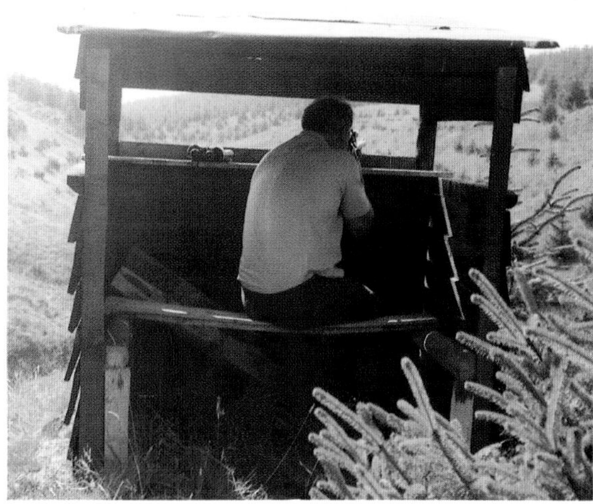

Hide

have a place where the ground configuration allows them to overlook favoured feeding areas and where control measures can be safely carried out.

Constructional details for high seats

The front and back are assembled first with the poles laid flat on the ground. All joints between the horizontal supports and the uprights are drilled and bolted and the diagonals are cut and nailed in place on the back. Notches are cut in two of the front uprights and the ladder rungs nailed into them. A continuous length of 10 gauge fencing wire is stapled over the ends of each rung for extra strength.

The front is then laid face downwards on the ground and the back propped up above it. The side horizontal members are then bolted on and the two diagonals cut and nailed into place. The structure is made more rigid if the ends of the diagonals are cut to fit flush against the sides of the horizontal members.

The high seat is then pulled upright by means of a rope attached to one of the upper horizontals. The floor is then nailed into place using the two round poles as supports under the floor. The sides can then be nailed on, the ends of the slabs or planks being cut to follow the line of the upright poles. A gap of about 300 mm should be left in the sides all round at a convenient height for shooting through. The seat can then be nailed in, again at a convenient height for shooting, using one or two planks supported at each end by the 1.5 m splits which are nailed between the upright poles.

Finally the two remaining 2 m splits are nailed across the tops of the upright poles and the roof timbers nailed across these. Alternatively corrugated iron sheets can be used for the roof or a sheet of polythene or roofing felt fixed across to make it waterproof.

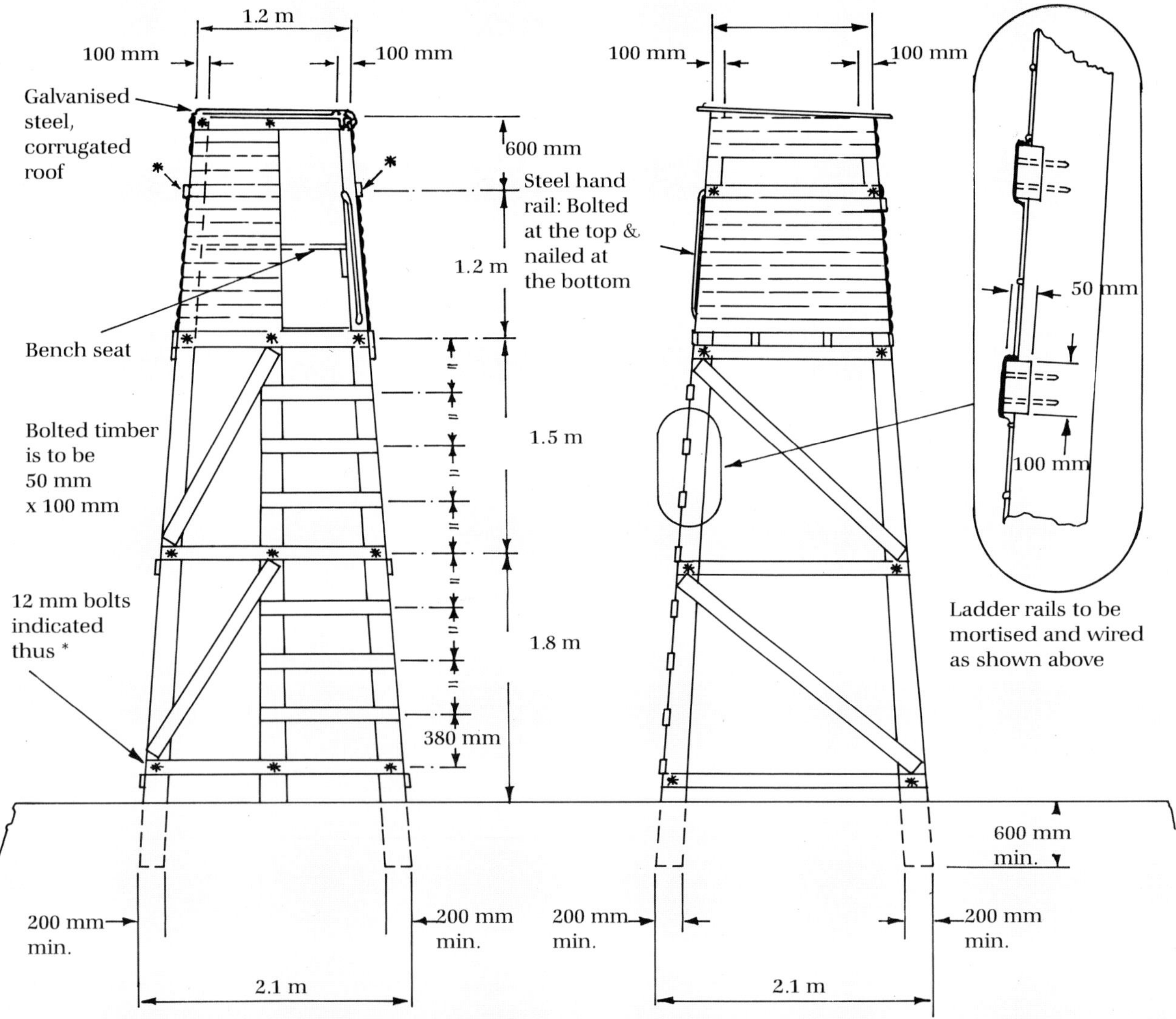

Note – All dimensions are in mm & m (not to scale)

Materials				
5	6 m	100 mm - 150 mm	Round larch poles	(Uprights)
2	1.8 m	100 mm	Round larch poles	(Floor supports)
6 approx	1.4 m	"	Larch splits (half round)	(Ladder rungs)
2	1.5 m	"	Larch splits (half round)	(Seat supports)
2	1.8 m	"	Larch splits (half round)	(Roof supports)
4	1.8 m	"	Larch splits (half round)	(Upper horizontals)
2	2.1 m	"	Larch splits (half round)	(Middle horizontals)
4	2.4 m	"	Larch splits (half round)	(Lower horizontals)
2	2.7 m	"	Larch splits (half round)	(Back diagonals)
2	4.3 m	"	Larch splits (half round)	(Side diagonals)
70 approx	1.8 m	150 mm	Slabs or 25 mm - 40 mm planks	(Seat, sides and roof)
10 m approx		10 gauge fencing wire		
23		230 mm - 240 mm approx coach bolts		
Assorted nails		100 mm - 150 mm and approx 40 large fencing staples		

The ends of the five uprights should be dug into the ground to a depth of 300 mm – 450 mm particularly where the site is exposed to strong winds.

I. Deer and the law

This chapter is not a full account of interpretation of the law relating to deer, but merely a summary of the more important legal factors which influence the management of wild deer, plus some points of Forestry Commission policy. For further details see Sections 7G and 7H.

1. The timing of the cull is primarily determined by the legal seasons (see table overleaf). Culling should only be undertaken outside these legal seasons (a) in response to serious crop damage, (b) in the immediate vicinity of the damaged crop and (c) with written authority. For this purpose the ranger should keep blank forms similar to the one shown beneath, which must be signed by the landowner and/or (on FC land) his forest district manager. (For Scotland see Section 7 H).

It may be added that, even to prevent serious crop damage, the Forestry Commission would rarely approve the shooting of an adult female deer between 1 May and 20 October, for fear of orphaning a young fawn or calf. Indeed, for the purpose of humane wild deer management, there is a strong argument for moving the female season for red, sika and fallow onwards a month (ie December–March inclusive) in England and Wales at least.

2. Deer may only be shot in the period of the day commencing one hour before sunrise and ending one hour after sunset.

3. In England and Wales the legal firearm for culling deer is a rifle with a calibre of a least .240 inches and a muzzle energy of at least 1700 foot pounds, firing a soft-nosed or hollow-nosed bullet.

In Scotland legal firearms for culling deer are defined by energy delivered, being in practice (for roe deer) minimum 50 grain bullet in a .222 Rem.; (for other deer) minimum 100 grain bullet in a .243 Win. Bullets must be soft-nosed.

In general the use of shotguns is prohibited for culling wild deer, except for humane despatch, or to prevent serious crop damage, nor (in Scotland) may they be used on unenclosed land. Shotguns used for preventing serious crop damage must be a least 12 bore, with minimum ammunition sizes differing slightly in England and Wales on the one hand and Scotland on the other, where a distinction is again made for roe deer (see Sections 7G and 7H).

Forestry Commission rangers will never use shotguns for the purpose of deer control, though they may be used for humane despatch of wounded deer (road casualties, etc).

(Name of ranger).. is authorised to kill deer out of season

in the immediate vicinity of.. *(name of place, fields, woods)*

in order to protect.. *(damaged crop)*

from intolerable damage.

(Signature of landowner).. (Date)....................

Deer close season			
England and Wales	**All dates inclusive**	**Scotland**	**All dates inclusive**
Red, sika, fallow, and roe (hinds and does)	1 March–31 October	Red, sika, sika hybrid and fallow (hinds and does)	16 February–20 October
Roe bucks	1 November–31 March	Roe does	1 April–20 October
Red, sika, fallow		Roe bucks	21 October–31 March
(stags and bucks)	1 May–31 July	Red, sika and sika hybrid stags	21 October–30 June
		Fallow bucks	As in England

(Muntjac and Chinese water deer not protected, at any time of year).

(Correct on 1 July 1993)

J. Taking the shot

High standards of deer management are maintained by skill and care in taking the shot. Two considerations should be uppermost in the ranger's mind when taking the shot: safety and humanity. These are achieved by observing the following guidelines:

1. ***Learn to handle the rifle safely.*** Do not carry a rifle in a vehicle with just the safety-catch on. Always have the rifle pointed in a safe direction, especially when loading. Do not release the safety-catch until you are in the aim.

2. ***Zero your rifle regularly.*** If you know it is accurate you will shoot with confidence. Do not use a rifle that has not been zeroed. Check the scope-mounting screws are tight.

3. ***Do not stalk without a dog available or accompanying, and a sticking-knife on your person.*** Train your dog to stalk with you if possible, otherwise it should be in the van near at hand.

4. ***Shoot from a good rest, such as a high-seat, tree or stalking-stick.*** Woodland stalkers should learn to carry and use a stick.

5. ***Do not aim through cover.*** Learn to check that the barrel, as well as the scope, is not pointing at an obstruction, especially that which it is resting on.

6. ***Do not take a shot, ever, without a safe background,*** nor risk hitting a second deer behind the first.

7. ***Do not shoot if, for whatever reason, your aim is unsteady.*** Breath out before squeezing the trigger smoothly. Never snatch or flinch.

8. ***Do not take chancy neck-shots.*** For neck-shooting, the deer must be near (under 30 metres for roe, under 40 for fallow and sika, under 60 for red), looking directly at you, and steady. Otherwise the heart shot is the only humane shot. Approach the deer for sticking immediately after a neck shot. If the deer struggles or gets up, shoot again quickly and without any reservations concerning spoiling the carcass.

Do not shoot

9. ***Take the heart-shot by preference in most circumstances,*** and ignore the advice of gamedealers and sportsmen to the contrary. The ranger's overriding responsibility is safe and humane despatch, not clean venison production. The essential point of aim lies 25 to 50 mm behind the shoulder and less than halfway up the body. But allow for the angle of the deer's stance, which should be at least three-quarters broadside. Be prepared to wait until the deer moves into position.

10. ***As the shot is fired, learn to note the reaction of the deer*** (see overleaf) and to make a mental mark of where the deer was standing.

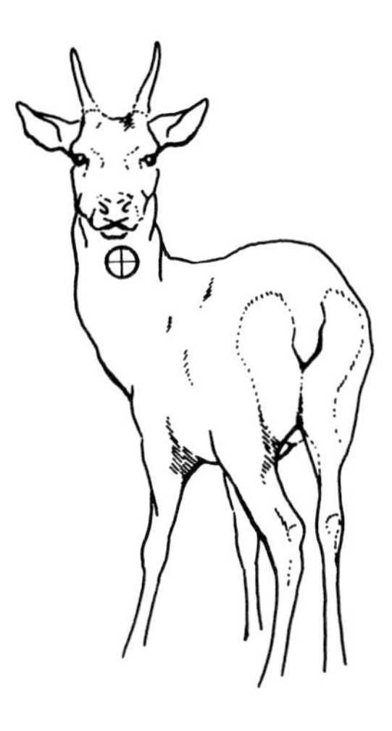

Point of aim

Point of aim

Wait till he turns
(Never shoot at head)

11. *Immediately after shooting, reload and put the safety catch on.* Do not forget this important safety measure in the heat of the moment.

12. *Providing the deer reacts normally, approach the spot where it was standing.* Mark the spot unless the blood trail is immediately apparent. Check for pins, colour and quantity of blood. Follow the blood-trail accordingly (see overleaf).

13. *Search for and approach the lying deer cautiously,* carrying your loaded rifle with safety-catch on, and be ready to administer a coup-de-grâce without hesitation if the deer shows any sign of life. Do not allow the dog to run ahead. Check the eye reflex for death. Return the bullet into magazine before putting the rifle down (not against a tree) at a reasonable distance, and sticking the deer. Double-check that the rifle is unloaded before sparing a thought for the death of the deer.

14. *Never assume you have missed until you have made an exhaustive search.*
Special care should be taken when culling sika, they show less evidence of the shot and can travel further than other species before collapsing. It is always advisable to follow through with a dog to avoid overlooking the carcass. For procedure with injured deer, See Chapters K & L.

15. *Remember there is always tomorrow.* Do not aim at the chest of a deer facing you (risk of bullet glancing off a shattered shoulder), the neck of a deer presented sideways (risk of

Point of aim

Two points of aim

injury to jaw, cutting windpipe or clipping spine), or at the head (risk of glancing injury to jaw and skull). Never shoot at a moving deer, except to kill a wounded animal.

16. ***If in doubt, for any reason do not shoot.*** Do not shoot beyond your personal capabilities, or when there is the slightest risk of the shot being unsafe or inhumane. Any fool can send a bullet on its way, but the greatest genius cannot bring it back.

K. Reaction to the shot

It is not always possible to describe the reaction of deer to the shot, as this varies with size and strength of animal, whether or not the deer is aware of the stalker before the shot, calibre of the rifle and other factors. The following are useful pointers, and a framework for experience.

1. ***Central chest*** (ie heart, lungs). The deer that reacts sharply to the shot, leaps or dives forward, and runs off quickly or wildly, and falls suddenly, legs kicking briefly, is displaying the average reactions to a good, fatal chest shot, especially near the heart.

The larger species of deer (especially red and sika) sometimes react less quickly to a shot which hits only lungs. So for these species, keep the shot well forward, and a little down. Note in the diagram how the heart lies further forward and lower than often supposed. It is almost impossible to hit the heart without hitting at least one shoulder.

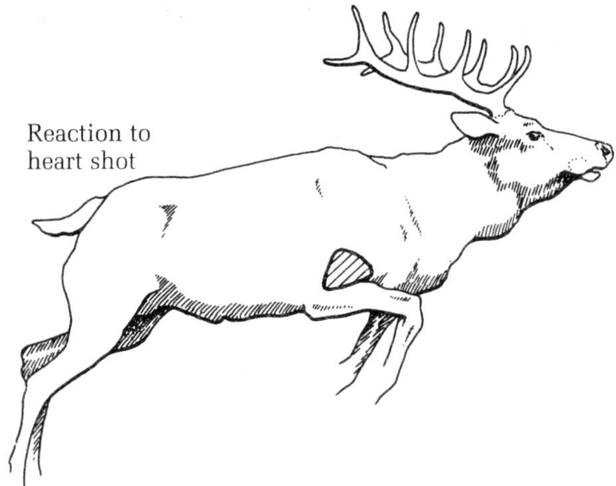

Reaction to heart shot

Shoot again

2. ***Neck.*** Deer drops instantly, but if there is any subsequent movement, especially vigorous struggling or movement of the ears, and the deer begins to get to its feet you must shoot again because once the deer begins to run you will almost certainly lose it without a dog, while the deer has probably received a serious injury. For these reasons the ranger or professional stalker reserves the neck-shot for close and steady shots, and does not neck-shoot unless the deer is face-on or broadside.

3. ***Backward of chest.*** The deer that is hit somewhere between the back of the lungs and the front of the stomach may react in different ways. If it is hit in the liver it usually reacts almost as for a heart shot, plunging away (sometimes after a slight shudder) and often running more than 100 metres. If the shot has done less damage to the back lobes of the lung, liver and spleen (and touched the stomach as well) the deer may react far less sharply to the shot, especially the larger species, possibly running off and lying down, possibly standing still or inching forward in a slightly hunched position. Be prepared in this case to treat as a gut-shot and to shoot again before final approach, certainly if the deer is lying, clearly still alive, licking the wound and rolling its head.

4. ***High shot.*** Deer drops instantly but in some cases clearly not dead. If it has been hit only through the crests of the spine, signs of paralysis may be brief and the deer will then regain its feet after a brief struggle on the ground and run away, perhaps uncertainly, if not shot again. If it has been hit straight through the spine (as might happen with a shoulder shot that goes too high) without causing any fatal bleeding (mostly large deer only), the deer will be evidently immobilized but will require despatching.

5. ***Stomach and intestines.*** The true 'gut-shot' which has not seriously damaged the spleen, liver or any major blood-vessel may produce very little reaction in the deer as it runs off. But if the deer stops, it will be seen to hunch up. A deer that is hit even further back, in the small intestines or haunch, is said to kick out

Paralysed by spine shot

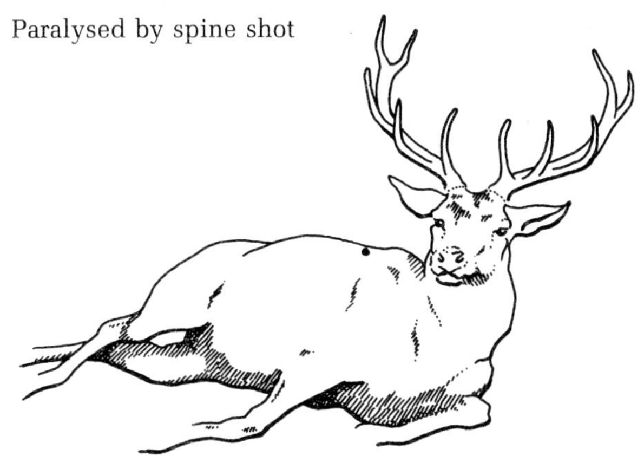

Reaction to gut shot

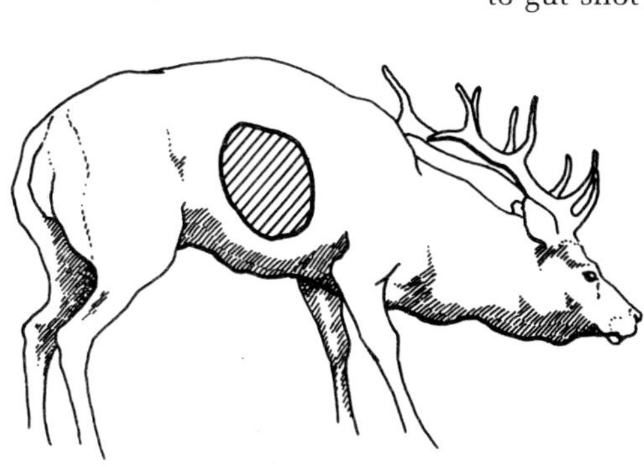

with its hind legs, or step backwards and sag, as an immediate reflex. In both cases shoot again immediately, as this is an animal which will otherwise suffer for a very long time. If it is not possible to approach for this second shot without the risk of chasing the deer further into cover in an unknown direction, mark carefully where the deer has gone. Leave it for 20 minutes to half an hour before pursuing the trail with your dog and rifle, which time should cause the deer to weaken.

6. ***Leg.*** If the deer drops or slides down, then runs away limping and carrying a leg, you have evidently broken a leg. Take second shot immediately, even at the moving deer if this is safe. Otherwise release dog immediately on small deer, or make delayed pursuit.

7. ***Clean miss.*** If the deer was unaware of your presence before the shot, it may not run at all, but flinch and stare around. If the deer was already aware of you, it will usually run off in the characteristic manner of that species. But never assume you have missed without an exhaustive search for a blood trail. Check for signs of the bullet, possibly on an intervening obstruction. Do not be the kind of stalker who tells himself that he has missed the deer cleanly if he fails to find a dead deer at once. Being aware of what has happened is the only way to reduce future errors and injuries. Indeed the individual stalker should be able to refine upon the above guidelines as a result of comparing reactions with where he has hit the deer.

L. Following a blood trail

If it is not immediately evident where the deer has fallen, it will be necessary to follow the blood trail.

1. Go to the spot which you have noted mentally as where the deer was standing when you fired. Mark this spot with a stick for future reference. Search around until you have found the ‘pins’ (pieces of hair), ‘paint’ (traces of blood) and other material (bone, stomach contents) resulting from the shot.

2. These may be very informative, even if you have not already had a good indication from the deer’s reaction as to where the deer was hit by your bullet. Bearing in mind that blood is brightened by oxygenation in the lungs:

a) Pink, frothy blood and spongy pink lung-matter gives a clear indication of lung shot.

b) Vivid red blood gives an indication of blood from the heart or a major artery.

c) Dark, brownish blood indicates blood returning to the lungs, quite possibly liver blood. If this is mixed with stomach contents the bullet has also burst the diaphragm.

d) A pure gut shot generally produces fluid and light watery blood as well as fragments of stomach contents (vegetable matter), usually in very small quantities only.

e) Look also for bone fragments (leg?) and examine the kind of hair which has been cut away by the bullet. You may be able to follow foot prints (the slot).

3. A large splash of blood followed by a strong trail with occasional splashes on the ground or surrounding vegetation is an obviously good sign. The deer will be found quickly, though it may have run a long way.

Obviously this does not mean that a sparse or short trail will not lead to a dead or dying deer. In particular it should be remembered that sika and red deer often shed very little blood, as though the wound seals up in these species. Most blood trails get sparser as they progress.

If the trail is very sparse and the indications are of a deer that has not died quickly, it is preferable to make a delayed pursuit, with dog and rifle, after 20 minutes to half an hour, a longer delay may cause the trail to become confused by the movement of other deer.

DON’T EVER GIVE UP ON A TRAIL.

M. Preparing the carcass

Only when the deer is dead, and the rifle rendered safe, does the presentation of clean venison become a priority.

a) The first act is to bleed the carcass by severing the artery at the base of the neck, then open the throat, free and tie the oesophagus and cut and free the trachea.

b) If the deer is being taken quickly to the larder, you may prefer to gralloch it there, but normally gralloching takes place on the spot. Remember to hide and split the gralloch. Also split the ribs and pull the pluck down if the deer is being left overnight or for any long period, if possible with the deer hung up.

c) The van should have a blood tray. During transport, try and avoid the deer lying in blood and dirt by placing some absorbent materials (eg leaves, newspaper) under the bleeding points. With care it will not then be necesssary to hose the carcass.

d) Keep hands clean throughout preparation. If possible clean carcass with a damp paper towel rather than by hosing.

e) A suggested method of preparation is: With the carcass hanging by back legs on gambrel, remove male genitalia or female udder to make first incision high up between back legs; open stomach wall to ribs and remove gralloch (this leaves 'gralloched weight'); split or saw down middle of rib-cage and insert spreader stick; remove back-passage and remainder of genitalia; cut round diaphragm and pull down liver, heart and throat in one; remove head (just behind back of ears) and feet (this leaves 'carcass weight').

f) Cool carcass to slightly above freezing (38°F, 3°C approximately) as soon as possible.

g) Remember that standards of cleanliness in a place where food for human consumption is being prepared cannot be too high. Hose down the entire larder, remove all gralloch in a bin, disinfect, purge of flies.

h) Record the weights, complete, gralloched or carcass as appropriate. The gralloched weight is the recognised weight for comparison nationally and internationally and therefore it should be accurately obtained and permanently recorded.

i) Remove and place in special containers any samples necessary for further scientific investigation, ensure that samples are properly labelled and recorded. Examples are blood, liver, kidney, muscle tissue from the neck, corpora lutea.

j) If the carcass is to be skinned it should be hung up by the back legs. Begin by cutting the skin up the inside of the back leg – point of knife under the skin from thigh to leg joint – part the skin from abdominal wall using the thumb and fist to separate skin from carcass, work up to top of leg and half round the back, repeat with other leg, take skin off tail then draw the skin down the back taking care not to tear the muscle or fat layers from the carcass and leave on the skin – a knife may be necessary in this process, cut the skin down the inside of the fore legs and remove the skin from them and the neck by drawing downwards.

k) If the skin is to be kept for curing the animal should ideally be skinned as soon as possible after being shot. The skin is then spread out to cool, hair downwards, common salt should then be rubbed well in (about ½ kg for a roe skin) paying particular attention around the edges. The skin is then folded into the middle from each side and rolled up, when kept dry and cool it will store for several months quite satisfactorily.

N. Preparation of heads and trophies

Heads for full mount

These should be skinned out as soon as it is practicable after the animal has been shot. The opening incision should be from mid-way between the ears along the centre of the back of the neck to a point mid-way between the shoulders, and then straight down to the base of front leg (elbow). The head is then severed between the skull and the atlas (first) vertebra, and either deep-frozen or well cooled and salted prior to taxidermy.

Frontal bone mount

Heads should be severed at the same point. Larger heads should be skinned, but with small species eg roe, this is unnecessary.

An electric boiler of about 30 - 40 litres capacity is ideal for this job, and heads should be boiled for an hour or more depending on size, until the flesh comes easily away from the skull.

At this stage the head can be cut with a reasonably fine-toothed saw. Care must be taken with small skulls, particularly yearlings, which are quite fragile.

A special saw has been developed for cutting roe heads involving a clamp which ensures each head is cut to an identical length and angle.

If the head is to be hand held it should

be placed with the back of the skull on a table or similar, the antlers protruding over the edge and the nose directly upwards. It can then be cut evenly from the point of the nose through the centre of both eye sockets, (short nose cut) or behind both (long nose cut), to the back of the skull.

All remaining flesh should then be carefully scraped away and flushed off with clean water.

When almost dry the head (keeping the antlers clear) should be soaked in hydrogen peroxide (preferably a strong concentration of '100 volumes' which can only be obtained from a chemist), for a few minutes and hung up to dry off.

O. Further considerations

So far, only the most essential elements of proper forest management have been considered. Once the ranger has begun to put this basic plan into practice, he will discover there is still plenty to find out! For one thing, the ranger who does not continue to walk his forest regularly will learn nothing new about his deer. One of the most important skills of the experienced ranger is to know where the deer in his forests are to be found at different times of year, and in which type of habitat and terrain to look for them.

Another skill in which experience plays a large part is the ability to assess the age and condition of deer in the field. The following are useful pointers:

a) Antlers are not simple indicators of age, but they are helpful once the ranger knows the deer on a particular forest.

b) Red stags usually grow knobs or simple spikes in their second year, though poor animals on hungry forests may not do so until a later age. Young stags usually grow brows, then treys, then beys and some crown, though at different ages on different forests. Old stags usually retain a heavy beam, but frequently begin to lose tines (especially beys) as well as body condition.

c) Fallow bucks almost invariably grow knobs or simple spikes in their second year. Young bucks usually grow brows then treys and increasing palm, though at different rates on different forests. Old bucks usually retain a heavy beam, but frequently begin to lose tines and breadth of palm as well as body condition.

d) Roe bucks often grow simple spikes in their second year, though on good areas they may already have forward (and exceptionally reverse) tines by then. As with other species, older bucks usually show heaviness of beam, especially in the base of the antler. An important tip at the beginning of the roe buck season is that yearlings are still in velvet in May or even early June, but have changed into summer coat by this time. Mature bucks remain in winter coat into June, but are in hard antler. Mature bucks are also stockier, hold their head and neck lower, and feed in briefer, warier snatches before looking around again.

e) Yearling hinds/does are usually detectable in the field by their uncertain behaviour and slimmer build. Mature deer have longer faces and are usually wary.

f) Whereas young deer are slender, old deer of both sexes appear sunken, and sharp in the sternum. They are often late in coat change and antler development (though the best bucks and stags all lose condition drastically in the rut).

g) Poor calves/fawns are short in the body, have harsh, gingery coats and retain their spots later than normal (see Species biology).

h) The only accurate measure of age is tooth development and wear (see illustration overleaf). It should be possible with experience to age animals accurately by teeth development up to 3/4 years old. After this age general tooth wear can give a guide only and can vary considerably depending on local feeding conditions. When examining a deer after shooting it is informative to note its fat reserves (kidney fat is a good indication) and breeding condition (lactation or pregnancy) in females. Correlation of such observations to judgements made before shooting is the only way for the ranger to improve his ability to estimate age and condition in the field.

One aspect of deer management which rangers may encounter from an early stage is being called out to attend to injured deer, especially road casualties. As these usually occur on busy roads, the ranger is well advised to attend these with a close-range weapon (shotgun with legal ammunition) as well as his deer-rifle. A rope (to secure the deer for despatch if it is only being prevented from running away by being held) and a powerful torch are essential equipment. Any deer which is incapacitated by an accident is invariably going to die, and should be despatched. Observe all necessary safety precautions, eg switch hazard lights on in FC vehicle, move people to safe distance, place animal in such a position that there is no risk of ricochet from the road. The shot should be aimed just forward of midway between the ears, at right angles into the skull, from as close a range as possible but with at least 1 metre between muzzle of gun and target. The

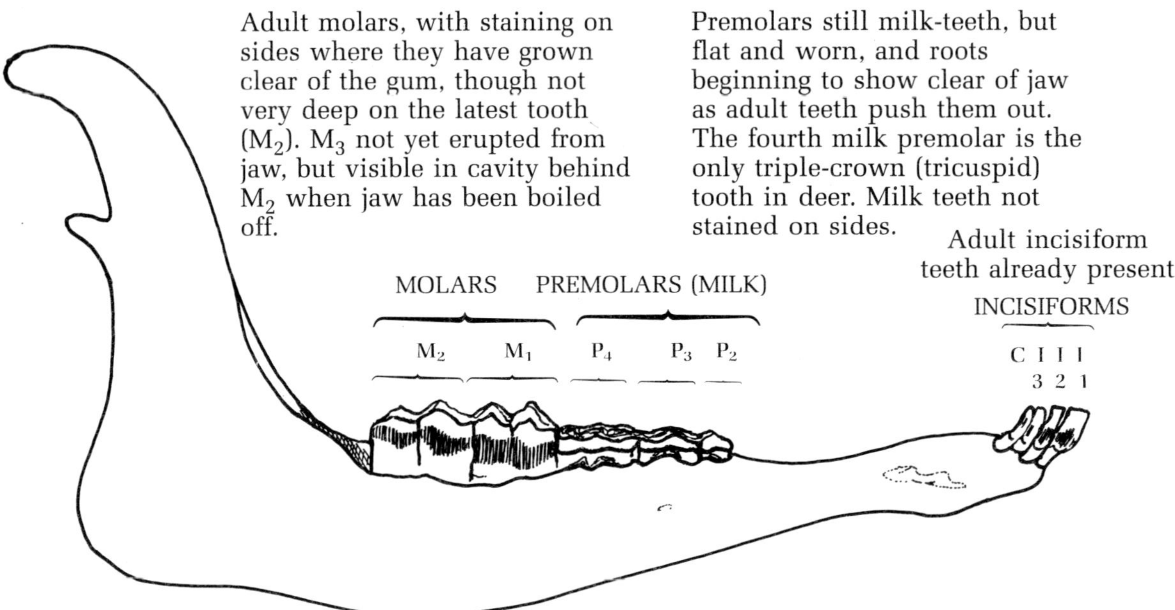

Fallow deer in second autumn i.e. approx 16-18 month old. Male (slightly smaller than life, approx. 15/16 scale).

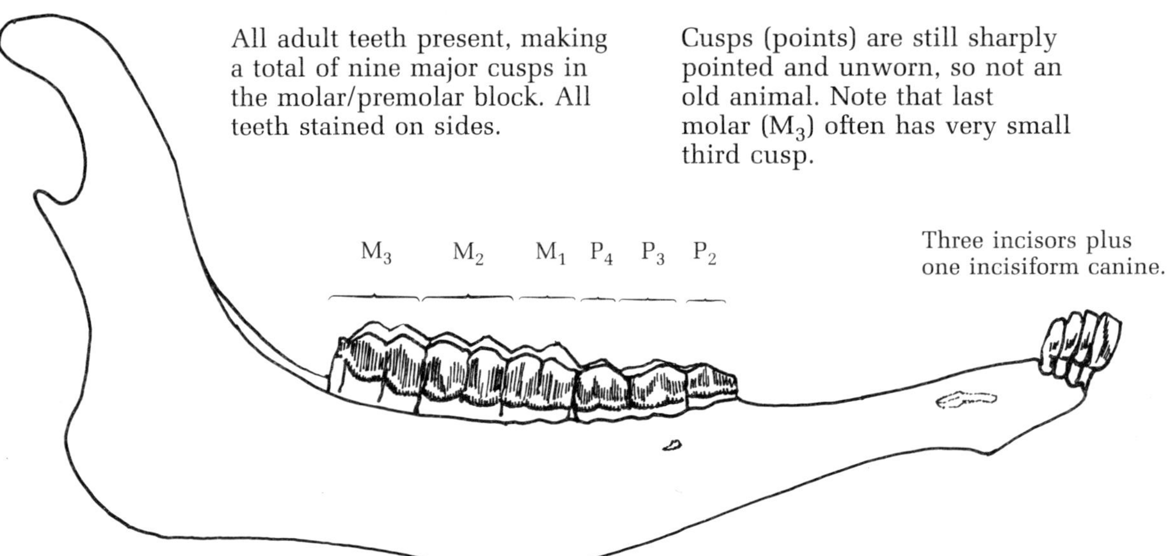

Fallow deer of approximately 3½ years of age. Female (roughly to scale).

only effective preventive measure is the erection of 'deer mirrors', by agreement with the County Council. They usually reduce accidents to about a third on stretches of road where casualties occur commonly.

Deer know no boundaries, and an important part of a ranger's duties is to liaise with surrounding landowners as necessary. Where these landowners are willing to have their deer included in the Forestry Commission management programme, there are sometimes advantages to the deer management on Commission land if the Commission ranger provides these services. Indeed in some cases it may be irresponsible not to do so if required. Elsewhere, when other bodies undertake their own cull, across-boundary liaison may be facilitated by participation in deer management groups and deer control societies. The involvement of people beyond those with a direct vested interest in the deer (eg local police, forest workers, County Council rangers) is invariably of great assistance to the ranger.

The supervision of licensed stalkers is dealt with in Section 6.

Tooth development

Species	Age (in months)	State of incisors	of premolars	of molars
	Calf (0-12)	Milk	Milk	M_1
RED	Yearling (12-24)	Mixed	Milk	M_1M_2
	24+	Adult	Adult	$M_1M_2M_3$
FALLOW	Fawn (0-12)	Milk*	Milk	M_1
	(*occasionally in mature fawns front adult tooth has erupted)			
	Yearling (12-24)	Mixed*	Milk*	M_1M_2
	(*exceptionally in mature yearlings all adult teeth present)			
	24+	Adult	Adult	$M_1M_2M_3$
SIKA	are very similar in their tooth development to red deer. In all three larger species, deer aged 24-36 months can be detected by the lack of staining on the small third cusp of M_3.			
ROE	The process of tooth eruption and replacement is completed towards the end of the first year of life. It is usually only possible, therefore, to tell a kid from all other age groups by the presence of milk teeth.			
MUNTJAC	Can also be aged with ease up to 12 months: M_1 erupts at 4 months, M_2 at 8 months, and M_3 at 12 months, by which time all teeth are adult. It is possible to age an animal up to 14 months by extracting the upper canine tooth, as this 'tusk' remains hollow in the base until this age.†			

(† Information from British Deer Society Publication *Muntjac* by Dansie, 1983).

P. Summary

Deer management is an art as well as a job, and requires the maintenance of high professional standards. The aim of Forestry Commission deer management is to combine the welfare of deer with economic crop protection.

This can only be achieved by having a scientific understanding of the deer herd in question.

After training, the ranger's work includes liaison with landowners and foresters, acquiring a detailed knowledge of the deer's use of the forest, formulating an overall management plan appropriate to the species and habitat, and implementing forest design for efficiency of control. These are all essential aspects of good management before shooting begins.

At the moment of shooting the priorities are safety and humane despatch. Only after the deer is dead does presentation of a good venison carcass become an important consideration.

The provision of sport for permit stalkers (see Section 6 A) is always subject to the above management approach.

Long-haired fallow deer, a local variety discovered in Mortimer Forest in 1955 by future Head Ranger Gerald Springthorpe

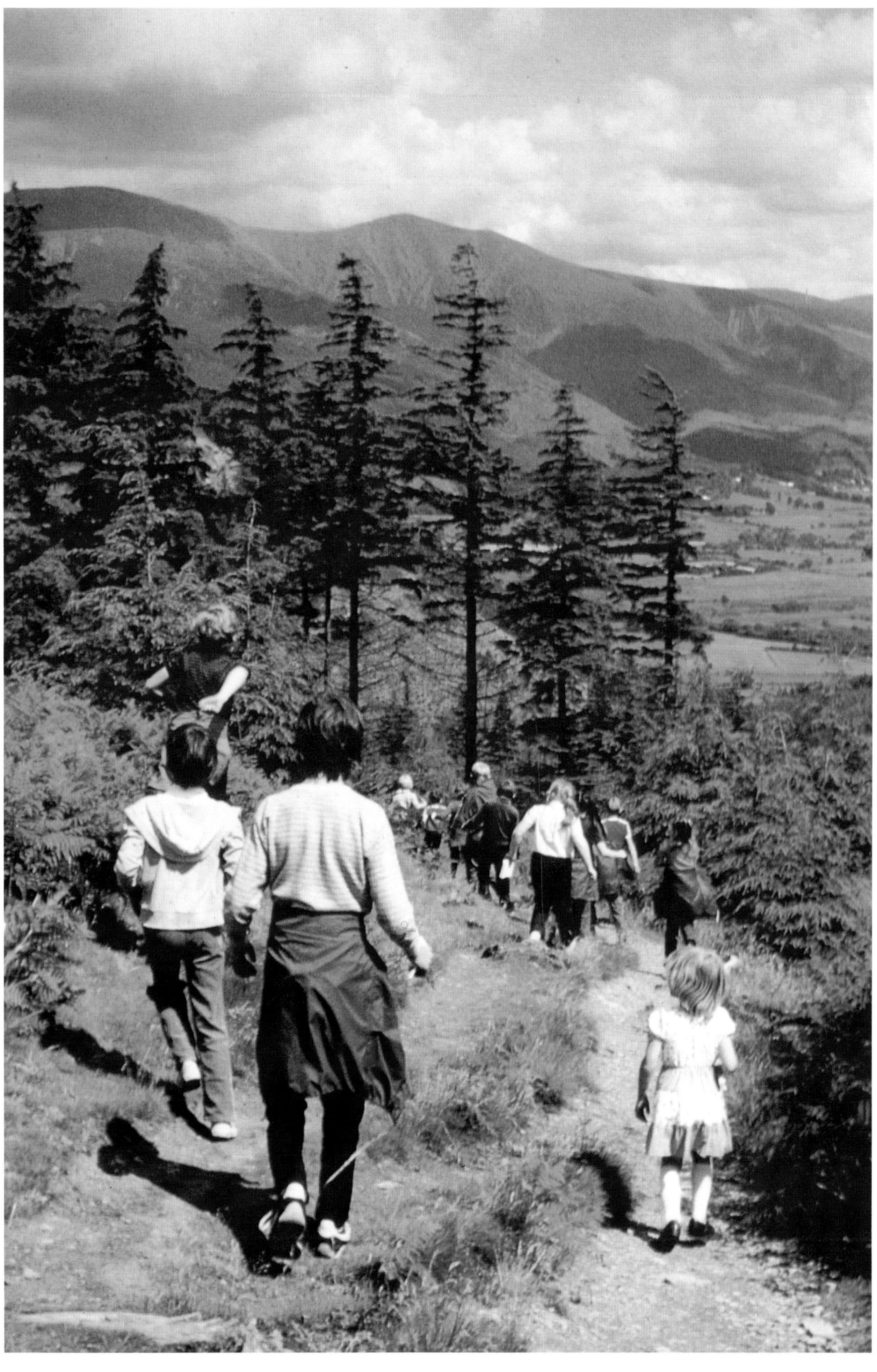

Section 5
The public

A. Recreation

B. Public speaking

A. Recreation

While it is true that many rangers are either wildlife orientated (concentrating on crop protection) on the one hand, or recreation orientated on the other, there is a considerable overlap of interests. The obvious example is the field of conservation, which might involve either breed of ranger (though perhaps the day is not far off when there will also be conservation rangers in the Forestry Commission!) In any event, wildlife rangers will be involved in recreation, guided walks and wildlife centres in many forests.

The situation of your forest determines the kind of visitor it receives, and broadly speaking forests may be divided into two types. Firstly those which lie near large industrial communities (eg Sherwood, Cannock) where the bulk of visitors are local, and secondly those which are situated in more remote holiday areas (eg Thornthwaite, Queen Elizabeth Forest, Glenmore), where the bulk of visitors are holidaymakers and tourists.

Taking the holiday forest first, it will be realised that the principal attraction of such forest is their scenery and habitat. Whether it be the New Forest, the Lakes or the Highlands, a majority of visitors have come a long way and some of them are prepared to walk a little further to enjoy seclusion and scenery. A fair proportion of them are prepared to, or even expecting to, spend some money. It is obvious, therefore, that facilities can include

i) medium and long distance walks, either in free access areas or on waymarked routes, with maps available to assist the stranger to the area.

ii) Interpretation centres and shops, where the tourist can buy and be given, as appropriate, Forestry Commission leaflets, Ordnance Survey maps, wildlife books and other items which may be taken away and enjoyed later, and which if well chosen are one of the best means of countryside education.

iii) A high level of services, such as toilets, caravan sites, picnic areas or even places where food may be bought. On the other hand, except outside permanently-manned facilities (shops, centres) and at special collection points on caravan sites, the idea of not providing litter baskets in car-parks is usually successful. It must be coupled with fairly frequent collecting sessions, but on the whole people do appear to take it away with them.

Turning to the industrial type of forest, it is clear that the local visitor is mostly interested in a brief evening walk, and he simply will not walk the same, short, well-worn and dog-soiled route every night. The best solution in this type of forest is to create a large number of small car-parks (without any special facilities) scattered around all the areas of the forest which the Commission is able to allow for people to visit. There is no need for toilets or elaborate route signposts, and indeed these merely lend themselves to the vandalism which will inevitably occur in these areas. Guided walks are popular in this type of forest.

The largest step forward which the Commission could take would be to introduce a dual system of access to its woodlands with no public access or free public access marked on all woods and maps. It may also be that we in this country have not gone anything like far enough along the road of urban park forests such as have been developed on the continent. Facilities such as an arboretum, wildlife lake, a deer park, a motorbike scramble track, a jogging track and a sports centre could be designed to heighten community involvement, and should be as self-maintaining as possible. The mistake which any ranger from an industrial forest could explain has been the attempt to import the countryside walk concept into the industrial forest, without any overall planning and zoning. The result is graffiti, vandalism, defacement, uncontrolled motorbikes, deer poaching, stolen-car joy-riding and a weak image for the Commission.

On either type of forest people's ability or willingness to walk varies considerably. On the one hand there is clearly a considerable demand for orienteering facilities. On the other there is scope for catering for the disabled. Horse-riding is another popular use for forests and in this case experience suggests that horse-riders and walkers should be zoned apart. The attempt to keep walkers and horse-riders apart on the same wood by means of marked routes is often a failure and the solution developed is to open up one wood for walkers to explore, and another for horse-riders. This is an example of the important principle of zoning land uses. One obvious point (though not always appreciated by planners) is that recreational facilities should not be brought into the best and most sensitive wildlife areas in the forest, simply because they will quickly be destroyed by the undiscerning and uncaring. The only solution is to keep the wildlife areas inaccessible and protected as sanctuaries, where they may still be discovered and observed by the more knowledgeable naturalist with permission.

The active involvement of the ranger in recreational facilities is far more important in the holiday forest than the industrial one (where, as suggested, facilities should be as self-maintained as possible). When on recreational duties, the ranger should be recognisable, well turned-out, friendly and (if necessary) calm and firm. After all, that is what he has been chosen and paid for.

Patience is often said by recreational rangers to be the cardinal virtue, and an interest in talking to others and identifying with their viewpoint.

B. Public speaking

The ranger is called upon to give a talk in a variety of contexts, but most of these fall into two basic types, (i) the forest indoor talk or lecture on a subject (eg wildlife and the Forestry Commission, Deer management) usually accompanied by slides, and (ii) the guided walk in the forest.

For the guided walk it is advisable to have a rough idea, at least, of where you are going to walk beforehand, and (if the event is advertised or pre-arranged) to warn participants how far the walk will be, whether they should bring a packed lunch, binoculars, walking boots, safety helmet etc. Also make it clear beforehand whether, for example, dogs will not be permitted (as is usually advisable). Indicate the meeting-place clearly (eg OS reference number, bus route, road from X to Y, etc).

If you can, include more than just talking and walking, eg arrange to visit a work-site and have the chain-saw demonstrated by a forest worker; start or finish at a forest centre or museum; place specimens on the intended route; visit a viewing hide where people can record in a visitor's book what they have seen.

Always bear safety uppermost in mind, and also explain forest safety regulations to your audience, eg keeping at least two tree lengths from a tree-feller, wearing safety helmet when inspecting bat-boxes.

For the lecture or indoor talk, make sure beforehand that it is clear who is bringing the projector, screen, extension lead, etc. If it is you, always take a spare projector bulb. Incidentally, do not entrust your talks or guided walks to memory. Keep a diary, also look at it regularly, and finally get the forest clerk to remind you from his or her diary as well. No talks go worse than the ones you fail to go to. Find out clearly where you are meeting, and arrive in plenty of time.

Both in the forest and indoors, make sure you are in a good position to address your audience. Stand with your back to the thing you are talking about, so that they look at you and it (the screen, something in the forest) at the same time. Never speak unless you are facing the audience. In the forest, do not start talking until you have gathered the group together. If there are serious stragglers, talk about something which is not vital to your theme, or devise a time-filling activity. If someone brings up an interesting point while you are walking, stop and involve the whole group. Do not just strike up a rapport with the friendly ones (or the pretty ones!)

There are two important points of courtesy. One is to dress sufficiently smartly for the occasion. The second is to introduce yourself clearly (name, position in the Forestry Commission) at the beginning of your talk.

For the rest, it is all a matter of common sense and technique.

The most important quality of your talk is enthusiasm for your subject.

For most speakers, the second-most important quality is spontaneity.

You will find that some of your best talks arise out of the most unpromising and unprepared circumstances. Never read from notes, and do not over-plan a talk or guided walk. Allow the slides or stopping points on a walk to jog your memory. Take immediate advantage of things that occur unexpectedly (eg a bird flying by).

Audience involvement is important. On guided walks in particular, draw your audience into the talking with questions and discussion. Testing your audience by questioning them on what you have said is a good technique. In a talk, if you have been interrupted in your stride, take the opportunity to summarise the important points you have made so far before continuing.

An important quality for most speakers is humour. In particular, try and put your audience at ease in the first few sentences. Throw in the odd story, and do not be dogmatic or take an over-serious view of anything. If you make a mistake, your best move is to make a joke of it.

Next, and more difficult, learn not to lose the attention of your audience. Do not throw them off the track by using technical terms they do not understand, and do not speak in a monotone. Say or do something unexpected!

Finally, learn the great art of saying enough and no more. When you have reached a high point in your talk, move on or pause, do not elaborate. Always finish your talk on a high note. After question time, have a few words or a thought to leave with your audience.

Section 6
Sporting management

A. Permit stalking for deer

B. Fish management

C. Wildfowl management

D. Liaison with shoots

A. Permit stalking for deer

Permit stalking on forest land provides a considerable amount of deer-stalking available to the sporting public in Britain, as well as an additional source of income to the Forestry Commission. What should, however, be quite clear in everyone's mind, as already explained in the deer management section, is that the provision of permit stalking is a secondary objective of deer management which must never be allowed to override the primary objectives of crop protection and humane management. This applies both in the detailed instance (eg the ranger should not turn down the opportunity to cull a buck on a damaged area in order to save the buck for licensed stalkers) and in general policy (eg permit stalking should be limited where rangers are struggling to carry out a large culling programme – especially on roe deer – when taking out permit stalkers can be time-consuming and counterproductive). On the other hand, these priorities of deer management in large-scale forestry do explain why a system of professional deer management with supervised permit stalking is always preferable to 'block letting' of deer stalking, as experience shows that adequate culls are seldom achieved by the latter.

The times to exercise permits are early in the season, while there is still a good choice of deer, or during the rut for trophy animals (especially roe bucks) if this is considered acceptable.

On arrival the guest stalker should be made welcome and given time to relax and unwind after his possibly long journey. Never go straight to the target range. Check the guest's credentials first (firearm and insurance certificates, FC Licence) and if, for example, there is a wildlife exhibit at the forest centre, this is a good place to take him and assess his general knowledge and appreciation of the subject in an informal manner.

At the target range, check the rifle and ammunition first (in good working order? especially safety-catch? Does all his ammunition match the rifle calibre? Is it a suitable type? Is the scope firm?). Ideally the client should fire a group of three at a target, then when you are satisfied the rifle is on, take a shot at a deer silhouette. If the rifle is off target, the ranger needs to be patient while assisting with the correction, as this is an important element in starting the relationship on the right footing.

The ranger must be firm but helpful so as to establish a friendly authority over the client. Now, before going out, is the time to ensure that the guest understands how the stalk will be directed by the ranger. Two points should be clearly understood, that the guest's rifle is absolutely safe, ie chamber empty, safety catch on, as he carries it following the ranger on the stalk; and that the guest needs to walk silently and smoothly at the same speed as the ranger. Make sure he comprehends and accepts that he must not make any move towards taking a shot until you say so. Unless you are sure of his ability, recommend him not to attempt a neck-shot.

All this time the ranger will be reaching a fairly good assessment of the client through general conversation, his equipment, his performance on the target range, and he will be in a position to plan the stalk accordingly, eg high-seat or very short stalks for the elderly. The stalking practice will vary with different conditions and combinations of forest to open ground and species of deer, however in woodland where there is high public access it is normal practice to stalk in the morning and sit in a seat in the evening. In any condition it is essential to check with the forester that there is no-one working in the area you decide to use.

Once in the forest, try and keep the guest in a relaxed frame of mind, as over-excitement or ill-temper leads to bad shooting. Bear in mind that it may be his only opportunity in the year to shoot deer, so he is often rather keyed up. You must carry your rifle. For one thing you may encounter a cull beast, and the permit stalker wants a trophy animal (in these circumstances it can be taken by the ranger and the stalking fee waived if no other beast is seen. In this way the culling programme is not being held back). In any case you need your rifle if a deer is wounded and for approaching the deer after the shot.

When stalking, the ranger should lead the stalk to within a safe distance (not more than 100 metres unless you have previous knowledge of the guest's ability), though the final approach may be made with the guest in front. Also when waiting for deer at close quarters in thick cover, make sure it is your guest who has the commanding view. Make certain that he is in a well-rested position, and be prepared to stop him for re-adjustment and a breather if he succumbs to a severe dose of buck-fever. Many guests will be hoping for your guidance, and most will know that they can benefit from it when given.

Avoid the following temptations:

- allowing a risky shot just for the sake of getting your guest a shot;
- leaving your guest unsupervised in order to move deer to him (what do you do if something goes wrong in your absence?); and
- shooting from a vehicle. Remember that

bad news travels fast, and the deer world is a very small one.

Be careful about protecting your own hearing. It is a temptation not to wear defenders, so that you can advise or help an inexperienced stalker right up to the last moment, and in these circumstances more than one ranger has received permanent hearing damage. The sound of a rifle shot is more powerful from the side, especially if it comes unexpectedly.

One of the ranger's most important tasks is to mark the position of the deer at the moment of the shot and if necessary leave the client at the shooting position to guide you to the spot. Take a bearing on any useful point. When sitting in a high seat, mark run from which the deer came out of cover.

After the shot, make sure the guest follows the correct drill (reload and engage safety-catch. Wait for a while in the case of body-shot). It is advisable to ask the guest to unload his rifle next, and make the final approach yourself, very cautiously, at least on the first occasion.

Remember to congratulate your guest and give him the opportunity of sticking and gralloching the deer. When all this has been carried out properly it is a good time to relax.

The way forward for permit stalking is for all guests to undertake a brief training scheme before they are permitted to stalk on Forestry Commission land. Such schemes are already in operation in some forests.

Finally, it is the ranger's duty to assess all clients at the end of their visit. A grade 1 assessment means the client could be trusted to go out on his own; grade 2 means the client is satisfactory under supervision; grade 3 means the client is unsatisfactory.

B. Fish management

i. Management objectives

The management of water for fish and fishing, whether streams or pools, has considerable potential in a forest context, but there are a few basic questions to answer before the creation and development of any fishing resources:

● ***What sort of fishing do the existing streams and pools lend themselves to best of all?*** Once again it is a question of making a proper assessment first, and we have already seen (Section 2G) that there are a huge number of variables in classifying the ecology of streams and pools, including speed of water flow, oxygen content, pH value of the water, water temperature, depth, quality of the bottom and nutrient supply to name but a few. It is always worthwhile asking the freshwater biologist and fishery officer from the appropriate River Authority to carry out a survey of the streams and pools under consideration. They can provide a detailed water analysis, indicate the potential food availability and offer expert advice on the species and number of fish required for satisfactory stocking, and any possible habitat improvements which could be made. The River Authority's consent is usually required if water is impounded when creating a new fishery, or when the movement of fish for re-stocking is involved.

● ***What sort of fishing is in greatest demand?*** In particular, where there is an option between coarse-fishing and game-fishing, which would be more appropriate? Game fishing usually involves a higher outlay, but can realise greater revenue. Coarse fishing can usually offer participation for a greater number of anglers on a similar sized fishery. It may well be sensible to conduct some market research on this and the following question.

● ***How will the fishery be administered and maintained?*** The clear option is between leasing the water to a responsible club, syndicate or angling society who then manage it independently, on the one hand; and retaining constant management and supervision within Forestry Commission control, on the other, with all the attendant responsibilities for issuing day permits (often at inconvenient times) and supervising the visiting fishermen who may well pose increased disturbance and litter problems without adequate supervision. In the case of game fishing, is the Commission ranger in a position to act as ghillie, and can the Commission police the fishery to protect it from poaching? Who is going to be responsible for stocking the fishery (if appropriate) and for what annual maintenance programme is considered necessary?

● ***What is going to be the effect on other forest activities?*** Clearly it is necessary to anticipate any drawbacks of opening up a fishery to the public, such as providing access to a difficult or sensitive area, or creating a clash with other activities such as wildfowling or general recreation.

ii. Fish conservation

Whether the intention is to realise a financial return from fish or not, the basic measures which help conserve fish should be carried out wherever possible. The habitats of freshwater fish may be divided very roughly into two main types: streams or rivers on the one hand, and pools or lakes on the other. These are considered in the following paragraphs with a few practical suggestions on habitat design and conservation.

(a) *Streams and rivers:* The brown trout and the migratory game fishes (salmon and sea-trout which mature and feed in the sea before returning to our rivers to spawn) command dedication and almost reverence from their devotees. The demand for game-fishing is high, in many areas its availability is limited, and the traditional beats can be prohibitively expensive. Many of our small rivers, though, in the forests of the Highlands and the north especially, could provide sport for the enthusiast if time and resources were devoted to their improvement. Indeed, as the game-fish streams are mostly in the uplands of Britain, where much of our forestry takes place, it could be said that the Commission has a special responsibility for the game-fish resources.

It is not always appreciated that even small upland streams of a metre or two in width are essential parts of a trout or salmon river, for spawning and a nursery for the young fish. What is needed in these streams is an even flow of water, rather than the extremes of flash-flooding and running dry. Trees in themselves help to regulate the drainage of water from watersheds into streams, provided that a considerate ploughing and drainage system is used. Both ranger and forester should study the detailed recommendations given on page 5 of FC Leaflet 78 (*The Management of Forest Streams* D H Mills) to avoid this problem and the inevitable subsequent criticism. It is also preferable not to carry out any drain cleaning operations during the period from mid-October to mid-May, as the eggs and alevins in the gravel of the stream-beds will be suffocated by the resulting downflow of silt.

It is essential not to plant the commercial forest crop right up to the edge of forest streams, but instead to allow the development of permanent natural ground vegetation on both banks, which serves to protect erosion, provide food for fish, regulate sunshine on to the water, catch debris from overland run-off and intercept toxic materials from thoughtless spraying. As considered in Sections 1A and 4F, such reserve areas (overall width on both sides adding up to roughly 10 times the stream width up to a maximum of 30 metres overall, with variations to suit the land form) have several other functions of forest design beyond their importance to fish. The development of taller vegetation such as alders, willow, ash and aspen is also beneficial in improving the all-important nutrient and food supply to upland streams, which are typically 'hungry' places, this being the main limitation on their fish stocks. Trees and bushes also assist bank stability, which, where necessary, can further be improved with re-inforcements such as large stones or gabions.

Of great importance is the creation of more pools down the stream length by damming to check the flow and create good holding pools to provide additional food and secure resting sites. These can take the form of simple rock and boulder dams or log weirs depending upon the availability of local materials at hand. (For details of constructing wing deflectors, bank covers and low weirs, see FC Leaflet 78 already referred to). It is important that dams (or any other construction, eg fences, culverts under roads) must be of such a nature so as not to impede the passage of migratory fish travelling upstream to spawn (details in FC Leaflet 78).

Such stream improvement techniques are usually all that is required to guarantee a good stock of fish, provided the natural spawning areas or 'redds' (as the gravel spawning beds in the fast water at the tails of pools are called) are kept clean and silt-free.

Coarse-fish streams and rivers are less frequently associated with forestry, but where they are the same principle applies of leaving good margins either side of natural vegetation. It is certainly beneficial for lowland streams to be shaded on some lengths by such species as alder. Whereas the fast flow of upland streams usually regulates aquatic vegetation, which may be allowed to fill 75% of an upland stream, in a lowland stream it may be necessary to reduce vegetation to an optimum 25% (see Weed management below).

(b) *Ponds and lakes:* The construction and general improvement of forest pools for wildlife has already been considered in Section 2G, including the necessity of deep water for overwintering fish. Considering the further design of a pool with fish specifically in mind, the requirements may be summarised as correct stocking density, optimum food supply, cover and suitable spawning areas.

Correct stocking density: If breeding conditions are good, a stage is quickly reached when there are a large number of rather under-sized fish in the pool. Re-stocking with quality fish will clearly only exacerbate the problem, and is a cardinal error in this situation. The answer is to keep records, with anglers noting down the length and weight of every fish they catch. Scale readings should be taken occasionally by experts to determine age and growth-rates, and from these observations it can be decided whether the water is overstocked. Should this be so, every effort must be made every year to remove as many under-sized (as opposed to young) fish as possible, either by angling, netting, trapping or electro-fishing. Careful weed-management (as detailed in the next paragraph) may also be the answer to striking a better balance between spawning and angling success. Harmful competition can also be reduced, while sustaining a greater number of fish, if the needs and preferences of different species are considered. Stocks which include both bottom, surface and midwater-feeding species can most fully utilise the true potential of a fishery. There may well be a place for predators such as pike and perch in such a system, especially in larger pools and lakes.

Food supply, cover and suitable spawning areas are closely related through the common factor of the vegetation in the pool. Water plants help to purify and oxygenate the water, they provide cover, shade and spawning sites for fish, and they sustain the many aquatic insects and other invertebrates on which most fish feed. Despite this, drastic weed-cutting is often embarked upon to make more space available to the fish and to eliminate angling problems. Some plants suffer badly and several years may elapse before they become re-established, whereas others positively flourish afterwards and become an even greater problem than before. It is sometimes essential to undertake weed-cutting to avoid a genuinely weed-choked fishery with excessive spawning, but weed-management, which is in many ways the key to successful fishery management, should be undertaken in an informed manner, and not blindly. The following guidelines are useful:

- Do not cut whole beds of plants, but keep fishing swims and deeper waters open by trimming and dragging on a little and often basis.
- Pond weeds can be broadly classified into two types, hard and soft, the more beneficial being the soft weeds. These soft weeds are bright green, fine-leaved plants that rarely emerge above the water but form a dense carpet that provides an abundant larder, eg water milfoil and canadian pondweed. Hard weeds (such as the water lilies and in particular the *Potamogetons* or broad-leaved pondweeds, which are emergent weeds with hard shiny leaves) are not only less food-bearing, they are invasive and can virtually swamp out potentially good fisheries, being extremely difficult to eradicate once established. Cutting is ineffective. They must be dug or dragged out together with the whole root system, and soft weeds can then be introduced to replace them.
- Sometimes the problem is not getting rid of weeds, but encouraging them. Weeds need clear, shallow water in which to grow, and in fisheries lacking plant growth and shallows (eg steep-sided pits and quarries) food supplies are severely limited and the fishing seldom good. Great improvements will follow if bays and shallows can be excavated around the margins. In such places the most productive water-plants can be introduced and supplies of shrimps, freshwater snails and Daphnia added to ensure a thriving future population of fish food. Remember that any pool maintenance is best carried out in the autumn months, to minimise harm to wildlife.

One other essential point of a successful fishery should be mentioned, and this is land-vegetation around the edge of the pool, which serves to screen the angler from the fish (often the dividing line between success and failure). Where such vegetation overhangs steep banks and deep water, as it should in parts only, there is another important source of insect food dropping into the water.

Most of the comments in this chapter on pools and lakes have been made with coarse-fish uppermost in mind. A pool which is kept for game-fishing (eg brown trout plus 'put and take' rainbow trout) needs to be well oxygenated by a good through-flow of water and should not have an excessively high nutrient input (eg from agricultural fertilisers) which might cause an overgrowth of oxygen-robbing algae in still summer weather. Game-fish are altogether less tolerant of pollution than coarse-fish. If trout, especially brown trout, are present, it is essential to allow them access upstream from the pool in order to reach spawning grounds. These spawning grounds need not only to be conserved, as described above, but also protected from possible harmful disturbance in well-populated areas and heavily-used forests.

C. Wildfowl management

As with fish, the purpose and effects of improved wildfowl management in the forest are never confined to the provision of sporting. They may be summarised as:

1. ***Conservation.*** Improvement of wildfowl habitats throughout the forest, and not just on the relatively few pools used for flighting. Increase in overall numbers and different species of wildfowl.
2. ***Recreation.*** The opportunity for the general public to see more wildfowl of different species, especially on the larger resting pools which are not shot, and may well be combined with observation hides or nature trails.
3. ***Sporting.*** Provision of extra sporting facilities with the advantages of professional supervision by the ranger and relatively cheap sport for those (especially younger) enthusiasts who are unable to afford a full gun in a shoot.
4. ***Forestry.*** The areas chosen for wildlife management will either be wet corners of the forest unsuitable for planting, or larger pools which have already been created for amenity purposes, and merely need improved habitat management for wildfowl. With intelligent and flexible zoning there is no need for any clash with other activities.

The known requirements of wildfowl are for mating territories, nesting cover (in suitable and secure habitat, not necessarily part of or connected to the mating territory which is being defended by the waiting drake while the duck sits on her nest), brood-rearing space and cover (if crowding occurs when the duck brings her brood back on to the water, there is a high mortality of young ducklings mostly caused by other ducks, even though feeding areas are shared). More generally wildfowl need rich feeding areas, undisturbed resting areas, and cover. It is particularly important that wildfowl pools should not be situated in areas designated for recreation and that they should be screened from roads and paths to give the wildfowl a sense of security and freedom from disturbance.

These requirements may be fulfilled by the following features of habitat design:

1. Most importantly, the shoreline should not be straight but sheltered and shaped by numerous bays and peninsulars. Also the more gently the bottom and margin of the pool slopes the larger will be the fringe of aquatic vegetation, reed-swamp and marsh which are the primary feeding grounds of dabbling ducks. A major advantage of a broken shoreline is that it allows pairs and broads to be out of sight of one another. It is known that a pair will be content with a small secluded bay (see sketch below for recommended size) whereas the drake will defend a far longer stretch of straight shoreline.

INDENTED EDGES OF A POOL

Even more importantly the chances of conflict between broods is reduced on irregular shorelines, which also provide shelter from the elements for the young ducklings. Another way of achieving the same effect is to design small, sheltered and shallow pools adjoining the main lake, or narrow 'cuts' running behind reed-swamp vegetation. In short, remember the 4 SHs for Shoreline: Shallow, Sheltered and Shaped!

2. The presence of an island or islands provides not only an increased amount of shoreline, but also the most important feature for nesting sites; protection from predators and from disturbance. Ideally islands should be shaped like a cross or a horse-shoe to offer maximum shelter. The best nesting cover is provided by short, thick vegetation such as dogwood, bramble, broom, gorse and tufted grasses such as *Deschampsia caespitosa.* Dense, secluded cover with food available is also required later in the year when wildfowl moult into eclipse plumage (ie dull duck-coloured plumage for drakes), for a short summer period whilst the flight feathers are regrown, as camouflage from predators. Artificial islands and rafts may be used in the absence of natural ones on very small tarns. (Details of construction may be found in numerous wildfowling and conservation publications, eg British Trust for Ornithology Field Guide No. 2, 'Nestboxes').

3. Another essential feature is that some banks, especially on islands and other shores away from human disturbance, should slope gently out of the water to allow wildfowl, especially ducklings, to walk ashore without difficulty.

4. Resting sites are essential features of wildfowl reserves, especially on any larger day-time resting pools of ten or more hectares. 'Loafing spots', as these are often called, "ideally consist of sheltered sand or shingle banks, where wildfowl can swim ashore to preen, sleep and sunbathe in security, or escape from rough water during storms. They also serve as assembly grounds for drakes moulting into eclipse in mid-summer". (J. Harrison, 1974). If it is necessary to control vegetation for this purpose, one method is to bury polythene sheets a few inches below the sand or shingle.

5. Larger pools and lakes can provide stretches of deep, open, water where (provided there is no regular human disturbance from boating, etc) ducks can also rest during the day, and where bottom-feeding species (eg tufted duck, pochard) can feed and rear their young.

Not all the pools in the forest will possess every one of these ideal habitat features for wildfowl. What is important is to have an overall plan of wildfowl management. It is, for example, essential to distinguish between large day-time pools (on which ducks can rest in considerable numbers) and small flighting pools (which may hold a breeding pair or two, but which, during the autumn and winter months, ducks visit principally at night to feed).

It is bad wildfowl management to use resting pools for flighting, or indeed to shoot at more than a limited number of flight pools each year. Some of the other small lakes, tarns, or lochans can be used for releasing artificially-reared ducklings (usually at 6 weeks) if required.

Pools should not be shot more than once a fortnight, and shooting should never take place without an adequate number of trained retrieving dogs. Finally, there should be a sensible and strictly upheld bag-limit for an evening's shooting, say 20 birds.

Important features of a small flight pond in the forest, other than those mentioned above, are flight paths which extend at least 50 metres in various directions from the pool cleared of any tall vegetation. Without these, ducks will be chary of using the pool, as they can see their exit routes are poor. Wildfowling hides, to provide concealment for the guns, should also be positioned in safe spots relative to one another.

The Commission must decide how wildfowling is to be supervised and administered in a given forest. The choice is probably less wide than in the case of fishing. In most circumstances it is preferable to reach an agreement with a local wildfowling club, as this is most likely to provide opportunities for enthusiasts who may otherwise find sport hard to come by. The alternative is to allow the formation of a small syndicate. In either case, an annual agreement will be drawn up. The ranger attends every shoot, so that he can provide guidance in good sportsmanship and safe gun-handling, while also collecting and receipting the agreed fee. All gun users must sign an indemnity statement.

D. Liaison with shoots

On Forestry Commission land there are two different types of situation in which shooting rights may be exercised. Firstly, where the shooting rights are held by the Forestry Commission and leased to a tenant. Secondly, where the shooting rights are held by the landowner (for himself or a tenant), or reserved from Forestry Commission ownership in some other way. The difference in practice is that the Forestry Commission has greater control over its own sporting tenants than over reserved shooting.

In the case of Forestry Commission sporting tenancies, both ranger and forester must be consulted by the Estates Branch whenever a tenancy is being offered for the first time or renewed, so that they may comment on:

1) Whether they consider the tenant to be suitable, because the highest bidder is not necessarily a greater asset to the Commission than a shooting tenant who may be trusted and who assists the ranger and forester in looking after the forest.

2) Whether there is any conflict between shooting and other activities (eg recreation) in the area being considered.

The ranger needs to be aware of the terms of the shooting lease. For example, whether or not tenants are permitted to use a rifle or to take deer. There is probably room for improvement in the standard Forestry Commission sporting lease, which could specify (i) a maximum number of shooting days in the year, and a maximum number of guns, (ii) that no shooting at all is permitted on Sunday. These clauses would be of value to the ranger and to wildlife.

In the case of reserved shooting rights, the person with the sporting rights and his gamekeeper should be quite clear that the Commission, as occupier, has the right of access to that land at all times. As with shooting tenants, the ranger should be supplied with a list of all shooting days, so he can avoid disturbing the area on those days. It must be understood, however, that the ranger cannot necessarily leave all his crop protection obligations until after the end of the game season, as some shoots imagine. While it may be possible for the ranger to notify the gamekeeper when he will be working in the area, the ranger must never be put in the position of needing to ask permission to go on. Moreover he can expect the gamekeeper to notify him if there are any fox-snares set. If deer are present, it is preferable if the keeper will agree to set the snares beneath snare bridges. (These comments do, of course, assume that the Commission has the deer-control rights in the area. In some cases this has not been provided for in the lease, leading to some awkward situations for the Commission – how does it protect its trees? – so in any new lease the Commission must at least secure concurrent rights to control deer. It is preferable, in practice, for the Commission to have exclusive rights to control deer principally for safety reasons). The Commission, as occupier, always has the right and responsibility to control ground game (see Section 3 C v).

The best means of avoiding any potential area of conflict is regular contact between ranger and shooting tenants, landowners and gamekeepers. Indeed, the ranger and the shooting interest can usually work together to mutual benefit, for example in developing rides and clearings, and in protecting wildlife.

Section 7
The ranger and the law

A. Explanation and caveat

The ranger needs a working knowledge of what he and other people in the forest and countryside may and may not do by law, and the following summary is aimed to cover the important points. It should be understood, however, that all details and exceptions cannot be included in every case. Further references may be made to the Acts of Parliament themselves, which are indicated by abbreviations in square brackets eg [1981 WACA].

This summary was believed accurate up to June 1984; notes on some important changes between then and July 1993 can be found on pages 118 and 124.

B. Firearms

i. Definitions

A firearm is defined [1968 Firearms] as any lethal barrelled weapon of any description from which any shot, bullet or other missile can be discharged, including (a) any weapon prohibited under Section 5 of the Firearms Acts 1968 to 1992, (b) any component part of a firearm, (c) and accessory designed to reduce noise or flash on a firearm, eg silencer.

Ammunition is defined as ammunition for any firearm, including grenade, bomb or other missile, whether capable of use with a firearm or not, and including prohibited ammunition.

Nail-guns, alarm-guns, safety-line guns, rocket-signalling equipment (but not Very pistol) and net-propelling guns are not regarded as firearms, and the provisions of the Firearms Act do not apply to a genuine (not reproduction) antique firearm possessed or sold purely as a curiosity or ornament.

Comment: It will be seen that a firearm can be discharged by any means (eg gas pressure, gunpowder, spring). A crossbow is not a firearm because it does not have a barrel.

ii. Certificates

A firearm certificate is needed to acquire or possess any firearm specified in Section I of the 1968 Firearm Act. These include: any rifle, revolver, pistol, humane killer, some flare signal guns, gas operated gun, prohibited weapon, Very pistol, sound and flash moderator, component working part or ammunition for any of above, any smooth bore gun which has a barrel with a length of less than 24 inches or a bore greater than two inches in diameter, or which has a non-detachable magazine capable of holding more than two cartridges, or a detachable magazine, shotgun cartridge which contains less than 5 pieces of shot or shot exceeding .36" diameter, or blank ammunition exceeding 1" diameter, also any air-weapon declared specially dangerous (with energy in excess of 6ft/lbs – pistol, or 12 ft-lbs – rifle). In addition to a firearm certificate, the authority of the Secretary of State is required for the possession of any prohibited weapon (other than a disguised firearm). This is not normally issued to private individuals.

The holder of a firearm certificate must sign the certificate in ink on receipt, take reasonable precautions to prevent access to the firearm(s) and ammunition by unauthorised persons, report theft or loss to the police at once, notify police of a change of permanent address without undue delay, and observe any other conditions attached by the Chief Constable (usually concerning limitations of use and place of use), or else commit an offence.

You may only sell or transfer any Section I firearm or ammunition to (a) a registered firearms dealer or (b) a person with a firearm certificate authorising him to acquire the firearm or ammunition in question or (c) a person who shows he is entitled to acquire or be in possession of it without holding a certificate. In the case of (b), you must make an appropriate entry on this person's certificate and comply with the instructions regarding sale or transfer (usually you must notify the chief constable of the sale or transfer of a firearm within 7 days by registered post or recorded delivery).

A shotgun certificate is needed for any shotgun (other than the above) but not for shotgun ammunition. The holder of a shotgun certificate must sign the certificate in ink on receipt, take reasonable precautions to prevent access to the shotgun(s) by unauthorised persons, notify theft or loss, and observe any other conditions attached, or else commit an offence. You may only sell or transfer any shotgun to (a) registered dealer or (b) person with shotgun certificate or (c) person who shows he may acquire or possess a shotgun without certificate.

No certificate is needed for an air weapon (other than one declared specially dangerous or disguised as another object).

The following are exempt from the need for a firearm or shotgun certificate (where appropriate, in connection with their business or occupation only): borrower of a shotgun in presence of an owner on owner's land; borrower of a rifle from the occupier of private premises on those premises under the supervision of the occupier or his servant; gun bearer or loader (but may not use gun); registered firearms dealer; user of gun at approved clay-pigeon shoot; member of Home Office approved rifle and pistol club or of a cadet corps; operator or user of miniature rifle range; person in service of Crown; holder of police permit (usually temporary eg following death of a certificate holder); carrier, auctioneer, warehouseman or their servant; licensed slaughterman; starter at athletic meeting; user of firearm borrowed for theatrical production; user of signalling equipment kept permanently on ship or aircraft.

A visitor to Great Britain may only possess a firearm or shot gun without holding a certificate if he is in possession of a valid British Visitors Firearm or Shot Gun Permit. If the visitor is a resident of one of the other Member States of the European Union he may also be required to produce a European Firearms Pass.

iii. Age restrictions

Section I firearm. (Person under 14) May not possess except as gun-bearer, in rifle club, shooting gallery or cadet corps. (Over 14 under 17) May, if holder of firearm certificate, borrow or accept as a gift.

Shotgun. (Under 15) May, if holder of shotgun certificate, possess either supervised by person of 21 or when secured in a gun cover.

Airgun. (Under 14) May not possess except at rifle club, shooting gallery or in a public place (not a pistol in this case) if supervised by person of 21 and secured in gun cover or on private premises may use air weapon if supervised by person of 21 provided missiles do not travel beyond premises. (Over 14 under 17) May not possess except at rifle club, shooting gallery or (not a pistol) in a gun-cover or on private property. May borrow or accept as a gift. May possess airgun ammunition.

It is an offence to sell or hire any firearm or ammunition to a person under 17, or to assist any juvenile in one of above offences eg if a father lends his rifle to his 16 year-old son who does not have a certificate.

iv. Other requirements and offences

- A constable may demand that any person he believes to be in possession of any Section I firearm or ammunition, or of a shotgun, should produce his certificate.
- It is an offence to discharge any firearm within 15 metres of the centre of a highway (not footpath or bridleway) and thereby injure, interrupt or endanger any user of the highway, or damage the highway [1959 Highway].
- It is an offence to have a Section I firearm with ammunition, or any loaded shotgun or airgun, in a public place without lawful authority or reasonable excuse.
- It is an offence to be drunk in possession of a loaded firearm [Licensing 1872] or to sell or transfer any firearm or ammunition to, or repair any firearm for, any person whom you believe to be drunk or of unsound mind.
- It is an offence to trespass with a firearm (police officer may arrest).

C. Wildlife (general)

i. Ownership and liability

Living wild animals of any kind are not considered to be the property of anyone, nor can they therefore be stolen, unless tamed or kept in captivity (eg pheasants in a pen) (1968 Theft).

On the other hand, dead wild animals are fully owned by the owner, occupier or sporting tenant of the land where they lie. (An exception arises when a person puts game up on land A and then kills it on land B, but permission will still be needed to retrieve it lawfully).

A landowner or other person is not liable for the actions of any truly wild animal (eg a deer which causes a traffic accident).

On the other hand, the Minister of Agriculture may serve a written notice on any person having the right to kill certain pest species (rabbits, hares and other rodents, deer, foxes and moles) requiring steps to be taken to kill these species for the purpose of preventing damage to crops, pasture, animal or human foodstuffs, livestock, hedges, banks or any works on the land [1947 Agriculture]. In the specific case of rabbits, an occupier of land is obliged to take necessary steps to kill on his land or (if this is not reasonably practicable) to prevent them causing damage [1954 Pests].

Comment: Clearly, the Commission, as occupier, would not wish to be placed in the embarrassing position of being served any statutory order, and it is, therefore, the ranger's duty to see that rabbits never get out of hand on Commission land, even if the sporting rights are not held by the Commission. Nonetheless, neighbours and sporting tenants must be expected to share their responsibilities for rabbit control, which clearly also arise from these laws (see also Section 4 C v).

ii. Traps and poisons

All wild animals are protected from being taken or killed by certain methods: Gin traps [1954 Pests], self-locking snares, bows and arrows, crossbows, explosives other than firearm ammunition, live decoys [1981 WACA].

The use of spring traps is restricted to a list of approved humane types, and even these may only be used in the conditions allowed for that type (see below for details).

It may be noted in particular that it is illegal to set any spring traps for hares, and illegal to set even an approved trap for a rabbit, except inside a rabbit burrow [1954 Pests. 1947, 1982 Spring Traps].

Moreover, while any trap or snare remains in position, failure to inspect it at least once every day without reasonable excuse is an offence [1981 WACA].

The placing of poisons in or upon any land or building is illegal, except in the following instances:

i) for the purpose of destroying insects and other invertebrates, rats, mice and other small ground vermin (including presumably moles) where destruction is necessary in the interest of public health, agriculture or the preservation of other animals, provided that all reasonable precaution to prevent injury to domestic animals and wild birds has been taken;

ii) seed dressings;

iii) gassing any burrows for the killing of rabbits;

iv) authorised gassing of badgers by Ministry of Agriculture personnel only, see below;

v) the use of warfarin on grey squirrels, but not in counties where red squirrels abound, see Section 4 E.

Even in these cases, it is an offence to use a poison which has been banned, namely elementary yellow phosphorus, red squill and (except for moles) strychnine, or to place poison on any land or highway where game animals or birds usually resort [1911, 1912, 1939, 1947, 1962, 1973 Grey Squirrels].

It is an offence to use an infected rabbit to spread myxomatosis.

iii. Licensing of prohibited activities

Several prohibited activities which are mentioned in the following chapters (especially in relation to the protection of mammals and birds) may be legalised by the granting of licences from the appropriate authority, eg

Activity	Authority
Bird ringing Marketing animals Photography, if otherwise prohibited Live capture of deer	Countryside Agencies (English Nature, Countryside Council for Wales, Scottish Natural Heritage)
Falconry Taxidermy	Secretary of State

Type and make of trap	Conditions
Imbra Trap Mark I and Mark II, both manufactured by or under the authority of James S Low & Sons Ltd, Atholl Smithy, Atholl Street, Blairgowrie, Perthshire and specified in British Patent Specification No. 682, 427 and as illustrated in figures 1 to 4 of that Specification.	The traps shall be used only — (a) for the purpose of killing or taking rabbits and set in rabbit holes, or (b) for the purpose of killing or taking grey squirrels or stoats, weasels, rats, mice or other small ground vermin, and set in tunnels constructed for the purpose.
Fenn Vermin Trap Mark I, Vermin Trap Mark II, Vermin Trap Mark III and Vermin Trap Mark IV (Heavy Duty) manufactured by or under the authority of Mr A A Fenn of FHT Works, High Street, Astwood Bank, Redditch, Worcester and specified in British Patent Specification No. 763, 891 and as illustrated in figures 1 to 3 of that Specification.	The traps shall be used only — (a) for the purpose of killing or taking grey squirrels or stoats, weasels, rats, mice or other small ground vermin, and set in artificial tunnels constructed for the purpose and, in the case of the Vermin Trap Mark IV (Heavy Duty) in either natural or artificial tunnels, or (b) for the purpose of killing or taking rats or mice and set in the open on their runs.
Fenn Rabbit Trap Mark I manufactured by or under the authority of Mr A A Fenn of FHT Works, High Street, Astwood Bank, Redditch, Worcester.	The trap shall only be used for the killing or taking of rabbits and set in rabbit holes.
Juby Trap manufactured under the authority of the Ministry of Agriculture, Fisheries and Food, Whitehall Place, London SW1, and specified in British Patent Specification No. 813, 066 and as illustrated in figures 1 to 3 of that Specification.	The trap shall be used only — (a) for the purpose of killing or taking rabbits and set in rabbit holes, or (b) for the purpose of killing or taking grey squirrels or stoats, weasels, rats, mice or other small ground vermin, and set in artificial tunnels constructed for the purpose.
Fuller Trap manufactured by or under the authority of Fuller Engineering Ltd., Felcourt, East Grinstead, West Sussex, RH19 2JY.	The trap shall be used only for the purpose of killing or taking grey squirrels.

Type and make of trap	Conditions
Sawyer Trap manufactured by or under the authority of James S Low and Sons Ltd, Atholl Smithy, Atholl Street, Blairgowrie, Perthshire.	The trap shall be used only — (a) for the purpose of killing or taking grey squirrels or stoats, weasels, rats, mice or other small ground vermin and set in natural tunnels or in artificial tunnels constructed for the purpose, or (b) for the purpose of killing or taking rats or mice and set in the open on their runs.
Lloyd Trap manufactured under the authority of the National Research Development Corporation and specified in British Patent Specification No. 987, 113 and as illustrated in figures 1 to 3 of that Specification. **Note to the 1994 reprint** The Imbra, Juby, Fuller and Sawyer traps are no longer available.	The trap shall be used only — (a) for the purpose of killing or taking grey squirrels or stoats, weasels, rats, mice or other small ground vermin and set in natural tunnels or in artificial tunnels constructed for the purpose, or (b) for the purpose of killing or taking rats or mice set in the open on their runs.

D. Wildlife (mammals and other animals)

The law frequently groups wild mammals and wild animals other than birds (eg reptiles and amphibians, fish, insects) together as wild animals.

i. Protected species

(a) The following species are fully protected under Schedule 5 of the 1981 Wildlife and Countryside Act: bats (all species), otter, red squirrel, sand lizard, smooth snake, great crested newt, natterjack toad; bottle-nosed and common dolphin, harbour porpoise, burbot; chequered skipper, heath fritillary, large blue and swallowtail butterflies; barberry carpet, black-veined, Essex emerald, New Forest burnet and reddish buff moths; Norfolk *Aeshna* dragonfly, rainbow leaf beetle, wart-biter grasshopper, field and mole crickets; carthusian, glutinous and sandbowl snails; fen raft and ladybird spiders.

The terms of this protection are that it is an offence to kill or injure such an animal, or to disturb it in any structure or place which it may use for shelter or protection, or damage or obstruct such a structure or place, or to sell or offer for sale any such animal or part of it, live or dead. The only legal exceptions are:

1. Tending a disabled animal.

2. Humane despatch if there is no reasonable chance of recovery.

3. Disturbing an animal or its shelter if this occurs within a dwelling-house. (However in the case of bats, this only applies to the living-area of a house, and it is therefore illegal to obstruct, disturb or dislodge bats which are in a loft, shed, cellar or eaves without advice from the national countryside agency).

4. Accidental injury, killing or disturbance of an animal as a result of a lawful operation provided this could not reasonably have been avoided (but again this defence will not be allowed in respect of bats outside the living-area of a house).

5. Finally, an authorised person may kill, harm or disturb such an animal for the purpose of preventing serious damage to livestock, foodstuffs for livestock, crops, vegetables, fruit, growing timber, or any other form of property or fisheries, but only on condition that as soon as the necessity for control becomes apparent a licence is applied for from the Minister of Agriculture. Without this licence it is illegal to kill such an animal except, as an emergency measure, by shooting only, provided only that a licence has been applied for and not turned down. (See also Section 4 E v).

(b) The badger is fully protected in a law of its own, the 1992 Badgers Act (see also the 1981 WACA). The terms of this protection are that it is an offence wilfully to kill, injure or take any badger, or even attempt any of these actions; it is an offence to sell or offer for sale or possess any live badger (unless possessed before 25 January 1974); and there are additional offences of ill-treating any badger, using badger tongs, digging for any badger, and using any firearm other than a smooth-bore weapon not less than 20 bore or a rifle with ammunition having a muzzle energy not less than 160 ft/lbs and a bullet weighing not less than 38 grains.

The legal exceptions detailed in relation to protected animals in the previous section also apply in the case of (1), (2), (4) and (5). In addition the use of poison or gas is legal for killing badgers to prevent the spread of disease, but only under licence.

Comment: The legal position concerning badgers went through a period of flux after the 1973 Badger Act as a result of research implicating the badger in the survival of bovine TB, and public indignation over the measures taken. In particular it should be noted that it is no longer legal for a landowner or occupier to kill badgers on his land without a licence. After the legalisation of gassing to prevent the spread of disease in 1975, the Agricultural Minister gave an assurance to Parliament that licences would only be issued for this purpose to members of his own staff, and this assurance (though not stated in law) has been observed ever since. The former 'areas of special protection' for badgers have been abolished, as being unnecessary now that this protection extends to all badgers. On the other hand, the 1976 Agriculture Act empowers the Minister to define areas in which his staff may undertake the destruction of wildlife to prevent the spread of disease to farm livestock even without the agreement of the landowners concerned.

It may also be noted from test cases that, in view of the severe penalties attached to the Act, defendants are likely to plead that they were actually in pursuit of foxes. Evidence to contradict this defence is helpful.

ii. Partly protected species

(a) It is an offence to kill or even intend to harm any animals listed in Schedule 6 of the 1981 WACA by the following methods: any trap or snare; electrical device for killing or stunning; poisonous, poisoned or stupefying substance; net; automatic or semi-automatic weapon; device for illuminating a target or sighting device for night-shooting; form of artificial light or mirror or other dazzling device; other gas or smoke; sound recording used as a decoy; mechanically propelled vehicle used in immediate pursuit or for the purpose of driving or killing.

These animals are: badger, bats (all species), wild cat, bottle-nosed and common dolphin, dormice (all species), hedgehog, pine marten, otter, polecat, harbour porpoise, shrews (all species), red squirrel.

Comment: The only legal methods remaining for these species appear to be shooting, use of non-live decoy, and destruction of the animal's home or shelter. In some cases (eg badger, red squirrel, otter, bats) this is an additional proviso to the exceptions to protection.

(b) It is an offence to sell or offer for sale any species of British reptile or amphibian, or any part derived from one (eg a snakeskin).

Note to the 1994 reprint

● The wildcat *(Felis sylvestris)* and the red squirrel *(Sciurus vulgaris)* have become fully protected species included in Schedule 5 of the Wildlife and Countryside Act 1981.

● The 1992 Protection of Badgers Act consolidates the provisions of various previous pieces of legislation on badgers. In particular the 1992 Act:

– Protects the badger sett from any form of unauthorised disturbance.

– Places the onus on anyone caught digging at a badger sett to prove that they were not digging for badgers, rather than on the prosecution to prove that they were.

– Specifies the circumstances and method by which an authorised person from a recognised fox-hunt may obstruct a badger sett on the day of a hunt outing.

● The 1988 Firearms Amendment Act makes certain amendments to the 1968 Act, including making illegal the possession and use of certain types of firearms (such as semi-automatics), and tightening the procedure of issuing certificates for shotguns and other firearms.

E. Wildlife (birds)

1. With one or two exceptions, detailed below, it is an offence to kill or harm any wild bird, its nest or eggs. The terms of this protection include the possession or sale of any live or dead wild bird, or eggs, or part of these. The legal definition of wild birds does not include domestic poultry or game birds, except where specified below.

2. Thirteen species of wild bird may lawfully be killed by authorised persons at all times, and their nests or eggs damaged or destroyed: crow, rook, jackdaw, jay, magpie; woodpigeon, feral pigeon, collared dove; house sparrow, starling; black-backed gulls (greater and lesser), herring gull.

It is legal to sell woodpigeons and feral pigeons at all times, but not the others.

3. A few birds may be killed only outside a close season, namely:

Capercaillie	1 February
Woodcock (England and Wales)	30 September
Snipe	1 February 11 August
Inland duck and geese*, coot	1 February
Moorhen, golden plover woodcock (Scotland)	31 August
Foreshore duck and geese*	21 February 31 August

All these species may be sold between the 1 September and 28 February, with the exception of gadwall, goldeneye, moorhen and all geese, which may not be sold at all. In Scotland none of these species may be shot on Sundays or Christmas Day.

*Duck and geese in this context refers only to the following species: tufted duck, gadwall, goldeneye, mallard, pintail, pochard, shoveler, teal, wigeon; canada, greylag, pinkfoot and (England and Wales only) white-fronted geese.

Comment: None of these birds is a true game bird in the legal sense, although a game licen(is required to shoot woodcock and snipe, see game law below.

4. The rarer breeding birds of Britain, listed in Schedule 1 of the 1981 WACA, are protected by extra penalties. It is also an offence to disturb a Schedule 1 bird while it is building its nest, or is on or near its nest, or to disturb its young.

Comment: It would, for example, be illegal, without a licence, to inspect the nest of a barn owl if this is known to be in a nestbox, or to set out to photograph it if this might cause disturbance). See Schedule 1 overleaf.

5. The exceptions to this protection for wild birds are almost identical to those for protected mammals considered above, namely:

a. Tending an injured bird.

b. Despatching a dying bird.

c. Accidental result of a lawful action.

d. In the interest of public safety or health (not an exception for Schedule 1 birds).

e. To prevent spread of disease (not Schedule 1).

f. To prevent serious damage to crops, etc (not Schedule 1).

6. It should also be noted that, even where a person is authorised to kill a wild bird, it is illegal to use just about every conceivable method except a legal firearm, non-live decoys and destroying its home or eggs. The only exceptions in this case are (a) the use of a net or cage-trap to kill birds listed above in paragraph 2, (b) the use of a duck decoy which was in use immediately before the passing of the 1954 Birds Act, and (c) the use of a cage-trap or net to catch game birds for breeding.

7. It is illegal to keep certain species of wild birds in captivity; 1981 Wildlife and Countryside Act.

Schedule I – Birds which are protected by special penalties

Part I – At all times

Common name	Scientific name
Avocet	*Recurvirostra avosetta*
Bee-eater	*Merops apiaster*
Bittern	*Botaurus stellaris*
Bittern, Little	*Ixobrychus minutus*
Bluethroat	*Luscinia svecica*
Brambling	*Fringilla montifringilla*
Bunting, Cirl	*Emberiza cirlus*
Bunting, Lapland	*Calcarius lapponicus*
Bunting, Snow	*Plectrophenax nivalis*
Buzzard, Honey	*Pernis apivorus*
Chough	*Pyrrhocorax pyrrhocorax*
Corncrake	*Crex crex*
Crake, Spotted	*Porzana porzana*
Crossbill (all species)	*Loxia*
Curlew, stone	*Burhinus oedicnemus*
Divers (all species)	*Gavia*
Dotterel	*Charadrius morinellus*
Duck, Long-tailed	*Clangula hyemalis*
Eagle, Golden	*Aquila chrysaetos*
Eagle, White-tailed	*Haliaetus albicilla*
Falcon, Gyr	*Falco rusticolus*
Fieldfare	*Turdus pilaris*
Firecrest	*Regulus ignicapillus*
Garganey	*Anas querquedula*
Godwit, Black-tailed	*Limosa limosa*
Goshawk	*Accipiter gentilis*
Grebe, Black-necked	*Podiceps nigricollis*
Grebe, Slavonian	*Podiceps auritus*
Greenshank	*Tringa nebularia*
Gull, Little	*Larus minutus*
Gull, Mediterranean	*Larus melanocephalus*
Harriers (all species)	*Circus*
Heron, Purple	*Ardea purpurea*
Hobby	*Falco subbuteo*
Hoopoe	*Upupa epops*
Kingfisher	*Alcedo atthis*
Kite, Red	*Milvus milvus*
Merlin	*Falco columbarius*
Oriole, Golden	*Oriolus oriolus*
Osprey	*Pandion haliaetus*
Owl, Barn	*Tyto alba*
Owl, Snowy	*Nyctea scandiaca*
Peregrine	*Falco peregrinus*
Petrel, Leach's	*Oceanodroma leucorrhoa*
Phalarope, Red-necked	*Phalaropus lobatus*
Plover, Kentish	*Charadrius alexandrinus*
Plover, Little ringed	*Charadrius dubius*

Common name	Scientific name
Quail, Common	*Coturnix coturnix*
Redstart, Black	*Phoenicurus ochruros*
Redwing	*Turdus iliacus*
Rosefinch, Scarlet	*Carpodacus erythrinus*
Ruff	*Philomachus pugnax*
Sandpiper, Green	*Tringa ochropus*
Sandpiper, Purple	*Calidris maritima*
Sandpiper, Wood	*Tringa glareola*
Scaup	*Aythya marila*
Scoter, Common	*Melanitta nigra*
Scoter, Velvet	*Melanitta fusca*
Serin	*Serinus serinus*
Shorelark	*Eremphila alpestris*
Shrike, Red-backed	*Lanius collurio*
Spoonbill	*Platalea leucorodia*
Stilt, Black-winged	*Himantopus himantopus*
Stint, Temminck's	*Calidris temminckii*
Swan, Bewick's	*Cygnus bewickii*
Swan, Whooper	*Cygnus cygnus*
Tern, Black	*Chlidonias niger*
Tern, Little	*Sterna albifrons*
Tern, Roseate	*Sterna dougallii*
Tit, Bearded	*Panurus biarmicus*
Tit, Crested	*Parus cristatus*
Treecreeper, Short-toed	*Certhia brachydactyla*
Warbler, Cetti's	*Cettia cetti*
Warbler, Dartford	*Sylvia undata*
Warbler, Marsh	*Acrocephalus palustris*
Warbler, Savi's	*Locustella luscinioides*
Whimbrel	*Numenius phaeopus*
Woodlark	*Lullula arborea*
Wryneck	*Jynx torquilla*

Part II – During the close season

Common name	Scientific name
Goldeneye	*Bucephala clangula*
Goose, Greylag (in Outer Hebrides, Caithness, Sutherland and Wester Ross only)	*Anser anser*
Pintail	*Anas acuta*

F. Wildlife (game)

i. Definitions and game rights

The term game refers to certain wild birds and animals which are pursued for sport. Because, as we have seen, there is no ownership of wild creatures, the game laws seek to protect the rights of landowners or occupiers to take and protect game.

Game, in law, always includes pheasants, partridges, grouse, black grouse, ptarmigan and hares (main definition), and refers to these species alive or dead. Certain provisions of the game laws include other species such as snipe, woodcock, rabbits, deer and others; these cases being indicated below.

The right to take game is a form of property which belongs primarily to the owner of land, but which may be transferred or sold. When the land is leased, the exclusive right to take game transfers to the tenant as land-occupier unless specifically reserved by the landowner, except in Scotland where it remains with the landowner unless specifically transferred.

An important exception arises in the case of ground game, which means rabbits and hares only. Because these species can cause particular damage to crops and timber, a tenant as land-occupier always has the right to take ground game (the terms of which are detailed below), whatever the concurrent rights of any other party.

ii. Game licence and selling game

You need a game licence to 'take, kill or pursue, or aid or assist in any manner in the taking, killing or pursuing by any means whatever, or use any dog, gun, net or other engine for the purpose of taking, or pursuing any game, or any woodcock, snipe, or any other coney (= rabbit), or any deer' [1860]. Except

(a) the taking or killing of deer on enclosed land (as opposed to unenclosed moorland) by the owner or occupier, or a person acting with his permission;

(b) the taking or killing of rabbits and hares by the owner of any enclosed land;

(c) the taking of rabbits and hares by the tenant or other person authorised by the provisions of the Ground Game Act (see below) and also the 1848 Hares Acts;

(d) a person assisting a game licence holder, eg a beater or loader (but such a person may not, without a licence, use any equipment of his own, eg a dog, or fire a gun, or assist a gamekeeper).

(e) taking woodcock or snipe with nets or springes, coursing hares with greyhounds, hunting hares with beagles or hounds, hunting deer with hounds, member of Royal Family or HM Gamekeepers, or person required by Ministry of Agriculture to kill animals as pests.

You also need a full game licence to sell game to a licenced game dealer (main definition plus imported bustards). It is an offence to sell game to anyone else unless you are yourself a licensed game dealer, except

- selling hares if permitted to do so by Ground Game Act 1880;
- publican in England and Wales selling game for consumption on premises, if purchased from dealer;
- person authorised by magistrate to dispose of unlawfully taken game.

It is illegal to sell or buy a game bird after the expiration of 10 days from the beginning of its close season (does not apply to foreign game birds, or live birds sold for rearing or exhibition purposes). It is illegal to sell hares (unless imported) during the months March–July.

iii. Close seasons

It is an offence to take or intend to take game on Sunday or Christmas Day.

It is an offence to take game during the close seasons, which are:

Black game	11 December–19 August 11 December–31 August in Somerset, Devon and the Hampshire New Forest
Grouse	11 December–11 August
Pheasant	2 February–30 September
Partridge	2 February–31 August

Ground game on moorland or unenclosed land of more than 10 hectares: 1 April–10 December (but the occupier of such land may take ground game between 1 September and 10 December, without firearms, and join with the landowner in doing so for their mutual benefit).

iv. Ground game

A tenant, as land-occupier, always has the right to take ground game [1880]. The terms of this right are:

- Only the occupier and persons authorised by him in writing may take ground game, for which no game licence is required, and which they may sell.
- Only the occupier and one other person so authorised may use firearms for this purpose.
- The occupier or one other person authorised by him may use firearms to take ground game at night, if written authority has been given by the person (or one of the persons) holding the game rights on that land [1981 WACA].

● The only persons who may be so authorised are resident members of the household, employees on that land, and persons employed by the tenant for that purpose.

Naturally enough, if the tenant as occupier holds the game rights as well, none of these restrictions apply. If the landowner, or other persons than the occupier, possesses the game rights, he will have the concurrent right to take ground game as well as the occupier, including night shooting.

v. Poaching offences

By day [1831].

● An offence to trespass on any land in search or pursuit of game, including woodcock, snipe or rabbits.

● Any person connected with that land, or any policeman, may require such an offender to leave that land, to give name and address, to surrender any game. Failure to do so justifies arrest.

● If 5 or more persons commit the above offence, it is an extra offence. If at least one of these 5 has a gun, and any violence or intimidation is offered to an authorised person, it is an extra offence.

● These offences do not apply to any person hunting or coursing (such persons do, however, commit civil trespass if they enter land without permission).

By night [1828, 1844].

● An offence to unlawfully take or destroy game or rabbits on any open or enclosed land, including highways.

● An offence to unlawfully enter or be on any open or enclosed land (including highways) with any instrument (gun, net, etc, not dog) for purpose of taking or destroying game (not rabbits).

● Any person connected with that land may arrest such an offender and seize game.

● An extra offence to offer violence with any offensive weapon to an authorised person.

G. Wildlife (deer, England and Wales)

1. It is an offence to take or wilfully kill any deer during its close season (Deer close seasons shown in Section 5F); except – to prevent suffering of injured or diseased animal; to prevent serious further damage to crops, vegetables, fruit, growing timber or any other form of property on the land if there are reasonable grounds for believing this damage to have been caused by deer of the same species. By an authorised person only (occupier, or, with written authority of the occupier, member of his household, person in his ordinary service on his land, or person having the right to take deer on his land).

NB: Trial v Buckingham (1972). Decision of court suggests marauding deer must be shot on land where damage is occurring, not nearby.

2. It is illegal to take or wilfully kill any deer at night (one hour after sunset to one hour before sunrise) except to prevent suffering of an injured or diseased deer.

3. It is illegal to use any of the following for the purpose of injury, killing or taking any deer:

- Any shotgun or smooth-bore ammunition, except (i) for despatching a seriously injured deer, (ii) as a slaughtering instrument (in which at least 12 bore, barrel less than 24", ie Section 1 Firearm, at least AAA cartridge), (iii) an authorised person preventing serious damage to crops (exact wording as in close season above), in which case at least 12 bore, cartridge containing a single non-spherical projectile weighing not less than 350 grains, or shot not less than AAA.
- Any rifle having a calibre less than .240 inches or a muzzle energy of less than 1,700 foot pounds, or any rifle bullet other than soft-nosed or hollow-nosed.
- Any air-weapon.
- Any trap, snare, poison or stupefying bait, net, arrow, spear or similar missile, any missile containing poison or drug, except (i) a trap or net used to secure an injured or diseased deer to prevent it suffering, (ii) under licence, taking deer live for scientific or educational purposes only.

4. It is illegal to discharge any firearm or missile at a deer from any mechanically propelled vehicle, or use such a vehicle to drive deer, except with the written authority of the land-occupier.

5. It is an offence, without the consent of the owner or occupier of any land, to enter that land with the intention of taking, killing or injuring any deer; to take, kill or injure any deer intentionally; to search for or pursue any deer with intent to take, kill or injure it; to remove the carcass of any deer. Any authorised person may ask an offender for name and address, and require him to quit that land.

6. It is an offence to sell venison out of season (as usual, 10 days after the beginning of the close season allowed) or to sell venison to any person other than a licensed gamedealer, or to sell or purchase venison which is known or believed to have been taken illegally.

7. Licensed game dealers are required to keep detailed records of venison transactions in a form set out in the 1980 Deer Act.

8. The police have power to stop and search any person believed to have committed an offence detailed in 5-7 above, or any vehicle believed to contain evidence of such an offence.

1 to 4 [1963, amended 1981 WACA]

5 to 8 [1980]

9. A game licence for shooting deer is only required on unenclosed land (usually moorland).

10. Deer are not included in the legal definition of game. A game dealers licence and a game licence is required by law as an anti-poaching measure and the inclusion of deer in these Acts is not to be construed that deer are included in the definition.

Note to the 1994 reprint

- The Deer (Firearms, etc) (Scotland) Order 1985 introduced important changes. In summary only:

  – A similar restriction to that in England and Wales now applies to the circumstances in which a shotgun may be used to shoot deer; only on enclosed land; by an authorised person; to prevent serious crop damage. Restrictions on calibre and shot size also similar but not identical: at least 12-bore; at least 380 grain rifled slug or cartridge containing not less than 550 grains of SSG or larger; for roe deer at least 450 grains of AAA or larger.

  – Rifles: ammunition must be soft-nosed. Minimum calibres are not defined, but rather performances which in practice relate to minimum 50 grain .222 Rem. for roe deer, and 100 grain .243 Win. for any other deer.

- With regard to fisheries law, it should be noted that regional authorities have the power to, and do, amend the national close seasons in response to local conditions. By the 1989 Water Act and 1991 Water Resources Act, these powers are invested in the regional National Water Authorities.

H. Wildlife (deer, Scotland)

1. It is illegal to take or kill any deer during its close season (deer close season shown in Section 5F), except on arable land, gardens, permanent grassland (not enclosed moorland) or enclosed woodlands provided there are reasonable grounds to believe serious damage will otherwise be caused. By an authorised person only (occupier, or, with written authority of occupier, owner, owner's servants, servants of occupier or other persons normally resident on that land. Also any person authorised by Red Deer Commission).

2. It is illegal to take or kill any deer at night except in order to prevent serious damage on agricultural land or enclosed woodland (i) the occupier in person may shoot red or sika, or (ii) any person nominated by the occupier may be authorised by the RDC, provided no other method of control would be adequate, to shoot any species.

3. It is illegal to take or kill deer by any method other than shooting, but as yet there is no restriction on the type of firearm used.

4. It is illegal to take, kill or wilfully injure deer without lawful authority.

5. It is illegal to use a vehicle to drive deer on unenclosed land for the purpose of killing or taking them, or to discharge a firearm or missile at any deer from an aircraft.

6. It is an offence to sell venison to anyone other than a licensed gamedealer, or to sell or purchase venison which is known or thought to have been taken illegally.

7. Licensed gamedealers are required to keep detailed records of venison transactions.

8. The Red Deer Commission has powers (a) to require from any owner or occupier of land a return of the number of deer killed, and (b) to enforce the control of deer on any areas if they are causing substantial damage.

9. A game licence is required for stalking deer on unenclosed moorland, except when a person is authorised by the RDC.

I. Wildlife (fish)

1. Any person may arrest someone who is (or who, with reasonable cause, is suspected of unlawfully taking, destroying (or attempting to take or destroy) any fish in water which is private property or in which there is any private right of fishery, and may seize any article used to take or destroy fish. [Theft 1968 Section 32].

2. It is illegal to take fish by the following methods:

a) ***Salmon, trout and freshwater fish*** firearm, stone or missile; baited line from bank to bank; spear, gaff (except plain gaff as an auxiliary to rod and line) or any other instrument, whether or not used with rod and line, for foul-hooking (including rod and line); light; baited line left unattended in water; wire or snare; otter lath or jack (including any small boat, board or other instrument used for running out lines); fish roe.

b) ***Salmon and migratory trout*** seine or draft net shot or worked across more than three-quarters of the waters fished; nets (excluding landing nets) with a mesh size of less than 2 inches knot to knot on each side of the square (local fisheries byelaws may authorise smaller dimensions); the placing close together of two or more nets, or their use with a device, in such a way that the above mesh size is diminished.

c) ***Any fish*** explosive, poison, noxious substance, electrical device. [Salmon 1975 Sections 1-5].

3. It is illegal to introduce fish or spawn into inland water without written consent of the water authority. [Salmon 1975 Section 30].

4. In England and Wales the National Rivers Authority (NRA) has the power to make byelaws regulating fishing for salmon, freshwater fish and eels. The purposes for which byelaws may be made are laid down in the Water Resources Act 1991. Copies of local fisheries byelaws may be obtained from the NRA. It is an offence to take fish contrary to the requirements of such byelaws.

5. The water authority has the statutory obligation to regulate fishing by licence. It is an offence in any place where fishing is regulated by licence, to fish without a licence or contrary to the conditions of the licence. (Salmon 1975 Section 27).

6. The Salmon and Freshwater Fisheries Act 1975 specifies the following close seasons for fishing for salmon, trout and freshwater fish but also provides that the water authority may specify different local close seasons, or dispense with them altogether.

Subject to bye-laws, the close seasons are:

a. Freshwater Fish	14 March–16 June
b. Salmon (rod)	31 October–1 February
(other)	31 August–1 February
c. Trout (rod)	30 September–1 March
(other)	31 August–1 March

(Not rainbow trout)

It is an offence to fish during the close season.

J. Wildlife (plants)

It is not a theft to take Fruit, Flowers, Foliage and Fungi (the four 'F's) from any plant, shrub or tree growing wild on any land unless for the purpose of reward, sale or other commerce.

BUT

● It is an offence under the Forestry Commission bye-laws to "dig up, remove, cut or injure any tree, shrub or plant, whether living or not".

● It is theft to take any of the four 'F's if they are cultivated, eg a planted tree in a forest. [1968 Theft].

● It is theft to dig up any plant (wild or cultivated) on any land as these are things which arc part of the land, and therefore property [1968 Theft]. Similarly it is an offence for an unauthorised person to uproot any wild plant intentionally. [1981 WACA].

● It is an extra offence intentionally to pick, uproot or destroy any wild plant on Schedule 8 of the 1981 Wildlife and Countryside Act.

K. Dealing with offenders

The ranger is inevitably in the forefront of the necessary task of policing the woods. Like a good policeman, the first aspect to this job is to become well-known to the general public in the woods, through friendly contact, ie stopping to talk whenever possible.

Offenders may be seen as falling into 3 categories:

1. ***Genuine.*** Probably ignorant of law or bye-law, or very minor offender, eg picking flowers, dog running out of control.

2. ***Chancer.*** Probably aware of transgressing or recurrent minor offender, eg man walking out of woods with pea-sticks, man approached for second time with dog apparently hunting in reserved area, children stealing birds' eggs.

3. ***Obvious transgressor,*** eg man found on woods at night with gun, or stealing quantity of fencing stakes.

The approach to the first category should, without fail, be a purely friendly one, very often passing the time of day before explaining, almost as an apologetic aside, that the behaviour in question is not permitted and also why it is not permitted. Such an approach usually has the totally desirable outcome of not upsetting the person's feelings (especially in front of children, wife, friends) while creating respect for yourself and the Forestry Commission.

The second and third categories are far more varied. You may in extreme circumstances, judge it advisable to seek police help before approaching, eg a group of badger-diggers at night. Normally, however, the rule still applies that it is better and easier to progress from a conciliatory approach to a harder line than vice versa. If the person accepts your authority and their own position of wrong, there is no problem, and a warning may be sufficient. But the person may not do as you ask, may walk away, be sullen or even abusive. You must remain calm and firm under all circumstances, in which case the person may become more responsive. In other words, the category which the incident falls into is partly influenced by the ranger's approach.

In a situation where the person still refuses to co-operate, you must choose between merely noting the incident in your diary or notebook, or attempting to pursue the incident, and it is usually preferable to do the latter if the credibility of the Forestry Commission is to be maintained. In this case, you should note as many particulars about the incident and the person as possible, eg dress, build, age, appearance, accompanying dog. If you can take a vehicle number at the time or by following the person, this is ideal.

Seek the assistance of others, if present, as witnesses. However, it should be noted that, contrary to popular opinion, the private citizen (ie person other than a police officer) is not entitled to arrest anyone unless the offence, by virtue of its seriousness, is an arrestable offence (eg offence carrying possible first conviction of 5 years imprisonment), or because powers of arrest are specified in the law being broken. These offences have been indicated in the summary.

In cases where prosecution is possible, but it is considered inappropriate to prosecute, it is still essential to issue a warning, and to record the incident. The offender may be a lessor or his servant (eg a gamekeeper using poison illegally) or a neighbour, but this rule applies with equal force, otherwise you and the Commission may become accessory to the offence.

When writing a report of an incident in your notebook, record exact and full information (eg the place, even though you know where it is), do not make erasures or alterations (if necessary cancel a mistake with a single line and initial it), write continuously without gaps, otherwise the quality of your evidence is brought into question.

It will be clear from the above that the ranger is ill-prepared for his policing duties and any incidents which may arise if he does not carry the following: notebook or diary and pen; identification card; copy of bye-laws; radio. These are essential parts of ranger equipment, of which the most important is his notebook.

Recommended reading

A. Recommended identification guides

The Wild Flowers of Britain and N.W. Europe. Fitter, Fitter and Blamey. Collins.
The Wild Flower Key. Francis Rose. Warne.
Birds of Britain and Europe. Peterson, Mountford and Hollom. Collins.
The Popular Handbook of British Birds. P.A.D. Hollom. Witherby.
Field Guide to the Insects of Britain and N. Europe. Chinery. Collins.
The Tree Key. Edlin. Warne.
Handbook of British Mammals. Corbet and Southern. Blackwell.
Collins Guide to Grasses, Sedges, Rushes and Ferns. Fitter and Fitter. Collins.

B. Further reading to sections of handbook

Section 1
Forestry Practice. Forestry Commission Handbook 6.
Forest Nature Conservation Guidelines. FC 1989.
Forest Landscape Design Guidelines. FC 1994
Lowland Landscape Design Guidelines. FC 1992.

Section 2
Trees and Woodlands in the British Landscape. Rackham. Dent.
Britain's Green Mantle. Tansley. George, Allen and Unwin.
Highlands and Islands. Fraser Darling and Morton Boyd. Fontana.
Habitat Management for Invertebrates. P. Kirby. RSPB.
Bird Nestboxes. (Field Guide No. 3). Flegg and Glue. BTO.
Bat Boxes. Stebbings and Walsh. FFPS.

Section 3
Forest Fencing. Forestry Commission Bulletin 102.
Assessment of Wildlife Damage in Forests. Forestry Commission Leaflet 82.

Section 4
Management of Red Deer in Upland Forests. Forestry Commission Bulletin 71.
Roe Deer Biology and Management. Forestry Commission Bulletin 105.
Glades for Deer Control in Upland Forests. Forestry Commission Leaflet 86.
Trees and Deer. Prior. Batsford.
The Culling and Processing of Wild Deer. Adams and Dannatt. Arun District and FC.

Section 5
Forest Recreation Guidelines. FC 1992.

Section 6
Forests and Water Guidelines. FC 1993.

Section 7
Countryside Law. Garner and Jones. Shaw and Sons.

Glossary of collective names of groups and voices for mammals, birds and other animals

Mammals

Name	Group	Name	Group	Name	Voices
Asses	Pace	Moles	Labour	Badger	Yells
Badgers	Colony	Mules	Pack	Dog	Barks
Boars	Sounder	Otters	Bevy	Red deer (calf)	Whistles
Cats	Clowder	Oxen	Team	Fallow buck	Groans
Cattle	Herd	Pigs	Drove	Fox	Yaps (dog)
Colts	Rake	Porpoises	School		Screams (vixen)
Conies	Bury	Rabbits	Colony	Fallow (fawn)	Bleats
Deer	Herd	Rabbits (young)	Wrack	Roe (kid)	Bleats
Deer (roe)	Bevy	Seals	Herd	Otter	Whistles
Dogs	Kennel	Sheep	Flock	Stag (red)	Roars or bellows
Elks	Gang	Stoats	Pack	Roe buck and doe	Barks
Ferrets	Business	Weasels	Pack		
Foxes	Skulk	Whales	School	Muntjac	Barks
Goats	Tribe/Trip	Wild Pigs	Sounder	Seal	Wails
Horses	Drove	Wolves	Pack	Sika stag	Whistles
	Harass			Squirrel	Chatters

Birds

Name	Group	Name	Group
Bitterns	Sedge	Magpies	Tiding
Chicks	Brood	Mallard	Flush
Choughs	Chattering	Nightingales	Watch
Coots	Covert	Partridges	Covey
Cranes	Sedge	Peacocks	Muster
Crows	Hover	Pheasants	Nye
Curlews	Head	Pigeons	Flight
Doves	Flight	Plovers	Congregation
Ducks	Team (in flight)	Poultry	Run
	Brace (a pair)	Quails	Bevy
	Flush (brood)	Ravens	Unkindness
Eagles	Convocation	Rooks	Building
Falcons	Cast	Sea fowl	Cloud
Finches	Charm	Snipe	Wisp
Game	Brood	Sparrows	Host
Geese	Gaggle	Starlings	Murmuration
Geese	Flock/skein (in flight)	Swans	Herd
Goldfinches	Charm	Teals	Spring
Grouse	Brood (single family)	Turkeys	Rafter
Grouse	Pack (large group)	Wigeon	Company
Gulls	Colony	Wildfowl	Trip
Hawks	Cast	Woodcock	Fall
Hens	Brood	Wrens	Herd
Herons	Sedge		
Lapwings	Deceit		
Larks	Exaltation		

Other animals

Fish

Name	Group	Name	Group
Clams	Bed	Jellyfish	Stuck
Cockles	Bed	Mussels	Bed
Dogfish	Troop	Oysters	Bed
Herrings	Shoal		

Insects

Name	Group	Name	Group
Ants	Colony	Gnats	Horde
Bees	Swarm	Spiders	Clutter
Flies	Business		

Reptiles/amphibians

Name	Group	Name	Group
Frogs	Colony	Toads	Knot
Snakes	Den	Vipers/adders	Nest